EUROPEAN SCULPTURE

DANIEL KATZ LIMITED

European Sculpture

Catalogue written by
Katherine Zock

CATALOGUE

1 CROWNED HEAD OF THE VIRGIN

FRENCH, LORRAINE
[Early 14th century]

Limestone
Extensive remains of polychrome and gilt
21 x 15 cm (8½ x 6")

Throughout the Medieval period the duchy of Lorraine acted as one of the buffer states separating the provinces of France from the territories of the Holy Roman Empire. Nominally subject to the German emperor until 1218, the duke of Lorraine then became a vassal of the count of Champagne and later in turn to the king of France. In spite of this political affiliation with France, Lorraine was able to maintain partial independence in the 14ᵗʰ century and the first half of the 15ᵗʰ. During this period it is fascinating, if not significant, to find the conditions that existed in the political sphere reflected in the sculpture of Lorraine, in its associations with other French styles and its distinguishing aesthetic association with Germany and the Rhineland.

The refinement and delicate precision of this *Crowned head of the Virgin* is typical of many works produced throughout the first quarter of the 14ᵗʰ century in the northeast region of Lorraine, and originates with the style at Amiens Cathedral (1225-1236). Distinctive from the dominant aesthetic that emanated from the Ile de France region, the production of Lorraine is characterised, in part, by its geographical proximity to Germany, and an infusion of a more northern typology. Aspects of a Rhenish or Cologne character can be seen in the present *Crowned head of the Virgin*, specifically in the prominent, rounded forehead above small features and the soft roll of skin between a sharp chin and neck. The figures on the façade of the Sancta Maria,[1] in Cologne bear strong stylistic comparisons to the present *Crowned head of the Virgin*, and are significant in constructing a stylistic vernacular across French and German territories.

The distinctive character of the Lorraine was first recognised in an article by William Forsyth[2] published in the Metropolitan Museum Studies in 1936, where he analysed the specific production of this northeast region basing them ultimately on that of the Saint-Dié Virgin, found in the cloister of the cathedral of Saint- Dié in Vosges and arguably the most famous of this type. While aspects of posture, drapery and variations on iconographic type played a consequential role within Forsyth's argument,[3] we are limited here in this fragmentary head of the *Crowned head of the Virgin*, to references of physiognomy, convincing enough, even alone, to place its origins amongst those outlined by Forsyth to the Lorraine region.

As with the *Virgin and Child* originally from the Church of Saint Maurice at Épinal (Vosges), now in the Boston Museum of Fine Arts, or the *Virgin and Child* from Châtenois (Vosges) in the Metropolitan Museum of Art, New York, the present *Crowned head of the Virgin* possesses a similarly definitive Lorraine disposition in its serene calmness, suggested through narrow, sharp cornered eyes

[1] The figures that decorate the façade and front portal are characterised by the same precise features and proportion, and the remains of polychrome suggest they would have been originally painted in the same naturalistic manner as the present *Crowned head of the Virgin*.
[2] FORSYTH, pp. 235-258, 1936.
[3] Aspects of drapery and variations of iconographic type distinctive to the Lorraine region of production are interesting, and carefully outlines in Forsyth's article.

[4] The entire collection was purchases by Duke University, America, and catalogued by Bruzelius and Meredith in 1991. This *Head of the Christ Child* can be found with illustration and text on page 203-4.

[5] Louvre, Paris. [Inv. S. 29] Illustrated *L'Art au Temps des Rois Maudits*, 1998, cat. no. 31.

[6] Victoria and Albert Museum, London. [inv. 7949-1862] Illustrated WILLIAMSON, 1988, cat. no. 37.

[7] Furthermore, instances where one sees the infant Christ holding a rose or floret, as in the definitive Saint-Dié *Virgin and Child* group, also points to a distinctively Lorraine idiosyncrasy.

RELATED LITERATURE:

Bruzelius and Meredith, *The Brummer Collection of Medieval Art*, Duke University Press, 1991.
FORSYTH, W., "Medieval Statues of the Virgin in Lorraine related in type to the Saint-Dié Virgin", *Metropolitan Museum Studies*, 5, 1936, pp. 235-258.
FORSYTH, W., "The Virgin and Child in French Fourteenth Century Sculpture", *Art Bulletin*, 39, 1957, pp. 171-82.
L'Art au tems des rois maudits Philippe le Bel et ses fils, 1285-1328, Galeries nationals du Grand Palais, Paris, 1998.
WILLIAMSON, P., *The Thyssen-Bornemisza Collection; Medieval Sculpture and Works of Art*, London, 1987.
Williamson, P., *Northern Gothic Sculpture, 1200-1450*, London, 1988.

with slightly puffy pouches of skin beneath and a nearly expressionless mouth; lips only slightly parted, and without the stereotyped sweet smile distinctive of the Ile de France production. This overriding solemnity of expression that distinguishes the Lorraine region of production, may be partly explained by a permeating Germanic aesthetic, and partly by a regional trend of refinement, typical to Lorraine and referred to today as the "atticism" of Gothic art.

A fragmented *Head of the infant Christ Child* from the Brummer Collection[4] has parallel features rendered with an almost fussy precision and highlighted with remains of polychromy similar to that of the present *Crowned head of the Virgin*; almond eyes accented with brilliant blue pupils, thin brow line over heavy lids and small red lips. Derived from the naturalistically coloured figures that adorn the front portal of Amiens Cathedral, today sadly stripped of much of their colour, the present *Crowned head of the Virgin* is exceptional in its superb preservation of original polychrome, permitting a clear example of how these sculptures would have been intended. Interestingly, it has often been noted that many characteristics of sculpture by the early 14th century are derived from ivory carving and manuscripts illumination, explaining some of the commonly observed gestures and postures and in this instance, helpful in understanding the specific use of applied polychrome; the choice of gilt strands of hair and such naturalistic features as rosy hues, like those seen on the face of the present *Head of a Virgin*, suggestive of blood running beneath the fleshy white 'skin' of her serene face.

The present *Head of a Virgin* wears the remains of a studded crown, suggestive of encrusted jewels, and the manner in which these precious stones are indicated by variously shaped protrusions of limestone is a further stylistic reference to the austere decorative techniques of the Lorraine region, and opposed to the more ornate character of the inset coloured glass examples seen throughout the Ile de France, as in the famous *Virgin and Child* group in the Louvre[5], or the *Virgin and Child* from Normandy now in the Victoria and Albert Museum, London[6]. Despite its fragmentary state, the crown of the present *Head of the Virgin* reveals a further sign of its Lorraine origin in the remains of the foliate motives that appear to sprout from the points of the crown, a version of crown design developed from the garland of entwined roses, idiosyncratic to the region and discussed in Forsyth's article.[7]

2 THE DEPOSITION

GERMAN, MAINZ
Possibly the
MASTER OF THE KREMSMÜNSTER

Fourth quarter of 14th century
Ivory and polychromy with traces of gilt
Height: 12.2 cm (5")

Fine overall condition.
Slightly concave back with incised cross-hatchings,
probably once part of a small altarpiece comprised
of many scenes with applied ivory figures.
Altarpieces of this type are scarcely known intact.
There is a hole through the top of the cross.

France was the dominant centre for the production of nearly all Gothic art, and while its hegemony encouraged itinerant carvers from all over Europe, and eventually a dissemination of trade and production by the middle of the 14th century, variations in style and technique remained minimal, explaining the problematic task of attributing these precious carvings today. Raymond Koechlin's seminal publication of 1924, Les ivories gothiques français,[1] *was hugely effective in clarifying the ivory industry of the period and the prominence of the Parisian carver, while offering for the first time a compendium of illustrated plates of Gothic ivories spread over the world's collections and museums. It is only until more recent research[2] that Koechlin's analysis has been expanded, and we begin to see emerging the idiosyncratic nature of the foreign carver, trained in Paris.*

It is challenge enough to place an ivory carving of the 14th century to a particular country of production, and quite a bit more unusual to ascribe a piece to a particular hand, as so few individual carvers have been documented or have stylistic profiles from which comparisons can be drawn. This well preserved ivory plaque of the *Deposition* is an exception, as both its technique of carving and iconography relates to a group of works in ivory believed to be by an anonymous sculptor from the Middle Rhine, whose style is ultimately derived from the diptych in Kremsmünster Cathedral, and reflective of the Commemoration Portal at Mainz.[3] Characterised by crowded compositions dramatised by unidentified faces, heavy drapery and the suggestion of abrupt, sometimes awkward actions, works by the Master of Kremsmünster possess a theatricality reminiscent of the *Mystery Plays* and emphasised by a certain degree of iconographic inventiveness beyond, yet not counter, to the accepted Biblical narrations.

[1] KOECHLIN, R, Paris, 1924. Based on newly discovered records of the ivory workers in Paris, the bylaws of their corporation, and bills and accounts of their widespread mercantile activities, Koechlin clarified the prominence of the Parisian ivory carver in three definitive volumes of text and images.

[2] For example; GABORIT-CHOPIN, D., *Ivories du Moyen Age*, Paris, 1978.

[3] RANDALL, 1993, p.11.[4] *Ibid.*, p.14.

Fig.1: German, attributed to the Master of Kremsmünster, *The Entombment,* Crocker Art Museum, Sacramento.

[5] Crocker Art Museum, Sacramento [inv. 1960.3.77] Illustrated RANDALL, 1993, plate 150.

[6] The Art Institute of Chicago [inv. 1943.60] Illustrated RANDALL, 1993, plate 149.

[7] The Walters Art Gallery, Baltimore [inv. 71.156] Illustrated BARNET, ed, 1997, plate 45. As representative of the Master's later work, compositional parallels can be seen between this and the present *Deposition*, while certain stylistic affinities are less comparable. The Master's style, although still being analysed, appears to have developed into more of an agitated carving style by the latter part of his production.

Identified by a definitive core of nearly twenty works, the *Deposition* responds to all areas of the Master of Kremsmünster's known vernacular. The bearded men that populate the background of the present *Deposition*, including that of the slumped body of Christ, Joseph who's bent back holds His weight, and the crouched figure of Nicodemus who removes the nails from Christ's feet, are all characterised by distinctively long faces with angular jaw, high cheek bones, sharp nose and deep set eyes. A technique of carving eyeballs separately from the corners of the eye socket is regarded as a specific detail of the Master of Kremsmünster's technique,[4] and finds no parallel in French production. This physiognomy is consistent throughout the Master's regarded works, especially prevalent in a plaque depicting the *Entombment* in the Crocker Art Museum[5] (fig. 1), another of the Dormition of the Virgin in Chicago[6], and a fabulous diptych leaf with the *Scenes of the Passion of Christ* in the Walter's Art Gallery, Baltimore[7]. The manner in which the hair of the men is carved, with a soft wave over the ears, and slightly unruly beards, is not immediately distinctive to those works by the Master of Kremsmünster, but on closer inspection varies from the more controlled treatment of hair characteristic to French or Italian ivories for example.

An ivory relief of a *Seated Scholar* (fig. 2) catalogued by Randall as Middle Rhenish, fourth quarter of the 14th century, displays marked similarities in style and technique to the present *Deposition*, and is also believed to be by the Master of Kremsmünster, or at least from his atelier of production. Parallel facial features with seemingly chiselled features and a beard that accentuates the length of the scholar's face and a treatment of drapery characterised by heavy folds that fall in

Fig. 2: Middle Rhine, attributed to the Master of Kremsmünster, *Seated Scholar,* fourth quarter of 14th century, Private Collection.

triangular creases, stylistically associates this plaque with the present *Deposition*. A distinctive anatomy, evidenced by the unusually bent arm of the *Seated Scholar* and that of the Christ in the *Deposition*, as well as the enlarged, crudely carved fingers of each figure is also analogous.

Aspects of costume, for example the floppy hats of the spectators and pointed shoes, are not distinctive to a particular region as one would expect, and can be seen equally in ivory carving throughout Europe, although more frequently in examples of a French origin[8]. Moreover, this particular scene from the Passion is repeated often, usually in a sequence of various Passion scenes of the type that this plaque would have once been a part, but is here addressed with postures, gestures and an individual characterisation typical to a German aesthetic, congruous with contemporary wood carving and monumental sculpture, and specific to the Master of Kremsmünster. There is no doubt that iconographic and aesthetic influences characteristic of Gothic ivory carvings ultimately emanate from France[9], and it is likely that foreign carvers, like the Master of Kremsmünster, were trained in Paris explaining the ease with which subsequent adaptations in style and technique have been overlooked.

[8] For example, the *Diptych with Scenes of the Lives of the Virgin and Christ*, Louvre, Paris [OA 9959]. Illustrated Barnet, ed., 1997, plate 25. Or *The Soissons Diptych*, V&A, London [inv. 211-1865].

[9] Earlier correlations between ivory carving and French architectural carving, like that above the portal at Rouen Cathedral, alabaster carving, as well as manuscript illuminations are many, and evidence of such visual influence is unarguable, while by the mid 15th century and the onslaught of engraved prints, a more distinctive character began emerging idiosyncratic to each country, and ivory productions from France, Italy or Germany, for example, become more identifiable.

RELATED LITERATURE:

BARNET, P, ED., *Images in Ivory; precious objects of the Gothic Age*, exh. cat., The Detroit Institute of Arts (9 March- May 11) and Walters Art Gallery (22 June-August 31), 1997.
GABORIT-CHOPIN, D, *Ivoires du Moyen Age*, Paris 1978.
KOECHLIN, R., *Les Ivories Gothiques Français*, Paris, 1925.
RANDALL, R., *The Golden Age of Ivory; Gothic carvings in North American collections*, New York, 1993.

ANTWERP, SOUTHERN NETHERLANDS
[Between 1490-1530]

Baltic oak with polychromy

36.5 cm (14") high,
47.5 (18½") cm length

The carved wood altarpieces produced in the South Netherlands (present day Belgium) between 1380 and 1550 are among the most lavish and splendid examples of late medieval art. During the period of 1500 through 1530, the Netherlandish carved retable manufacture reached its highest level of output, encouraged by a mounting international demand, and efficient division of labour within the controlled guild production of these altarpieces. One can trace the stylistic development of these sumptuous wood carvings, first in their response to contemporaneous indigenous painters and later by the affectations of the Italian Renaissance and Mannerism.

[1] All polychromy original and with no subsequent restoration. Paint analysis report available upon request. [Carol Hassall, London]
[2] Refer to illustration of Hakendover altarpiece, fig. 88, Jacobs, 1998, p.237.

This remarkably well-preserved group of the *Mourning Maries* is exceptional in its sophistication of carving and emotive effect, supported by the unusual amount of original polychrome.[1] The production of South Netherlandish carved altarpieces travels a distinct stylistic course beginning from around the year 1400 to the eclipse of their manufacture by the end of the 1550s. Beginning in an International Gothic Style, clearly represented by the retable of Hakendover,[2] the carved altarpiece develops gradually into a more Renaissance influenced concept until, by the final years of their making, they are pushed into the contorted, slightly caricatured personality of the Mannerist style. These variations in stylistic trend can be broken into four distinct groupings, the present group of *Mourning Maries* falling securely within what is marked as the second phase, characterised by a late Gothic style, distinguishable by an increased sense of realism, convincing postures and naturalistic features.

This progression from the refinement of the International Style to the more realistic late Gothic style of which the present *Mourning Maries* is an example, was in part inspired by the growing realism of early Netherlandish painting. The softening of the figure postures, convincing displays of emotion, and a more sensitive treatment of volume beneath folded drapery stem from the contemporaneous paintings of Robert Campin, Jan van Eyck and Rogier van der Weyden, painters who would have been exceedingly well-known and highly regarded as ateliers in the onslaught of realism that eventually became the hallmark of Netherlandish art.

The present group, showing the *Mourning Maries*, would have been originally part of a Crucifixion narrative. The separation of this particular group from its whole is made simpler by the way in which carved altarpieces were constructed by the late 15th century, and is an effective means of dating of this group. In earlier carved works dating from the late 14th and early 15th centuries, the figural scenes were typically carved out of one block of wood; but at s'Hertogenbosch, as in most later retables, the scenes are composed of several figure groupings, which are carved on separate relief planes and pegged together to form a running compositional narrative. This construction allowed a greater breadth of altarpiece scale, encouraged more complicated figural groups and facilitated the overall production rate in a market that was increasingly demanding.

The remarkable preservation of the *Mourning Maries* extends to its richly painted surface, where details of individual gold thread, ornate patterns and decorated borders suggests the finest clothes and costume. Particularly impressive in the present group are the naturalistic facial features, skin tone, and emotive expressions as seen through tearful eyes and parted lips. The carvers and painters of these Netherlandish altarpieces were different artists, of varying skill. Preserved documents prove that the guild system, especially within the towns of Brussels and Antwerp, were successful in establishing corporate rules and corporate identities, and that the overall expansion in the production of the Netherlandish altarpiece reflects this system, and helped to facilitate the integration of both painters and carvers on the same retable.[3]

Beyond the obviously high standard of quality in both the wood carving and painted surface of the present group, the presence of the Antwerp stamp, an imprint of a hand, proves its provenance, as well as its approved standard. In keeping with the international market demand for these Netherlandish retables, the centres of production, Brussels and Antwerp, developed a system of quality control in an effort to secure consistency and standard. Retables bearing the quality control mark, as in the case of the present example, would comprise the upper level of the market, and demand the highest prices.

Characteristic of Netherlandish retable production, is an overwhelming aesthetic continuity, and while there was an irrefutable transformation from the International Style to a more Renaissance influenced culmination, the Netherlandish altarpiece, as a whole, remains as an impressively lengthy wood carving tradition, strongly rooted in a late medieval sentiment and fervent religious value. It may well be argued that it is within this resounding sense of continuity that the market for the Netherlandish retable found its success. The present *Mourning Maries* represent the height of both Antwerp wood carving production and indigenous refinement.

[3] A useful chapter on the organisation of these guild systems is found in JACOBS, *Early Netherlandish Carved Altarpieces*, Cambridge University Press, 1998.

RELATED LITERATURE:

ENGELEN, K., ED., *The Antwerp Altarpiece*, exhibition catalogue National Gallery Victoria, Antwerp, 1983.
JACOBS, L., *Early Netherlandish Carved Altarpieces*, 1380-1550, Cambridge University Press, 1998.

4 THE PENITENT SAINT JEROME

ITALIAN, NAPLES

Marble
About 1500
62 x 32 cm (24½ x 12¼")

Saint Jerome is often shown as an aesthetic, specifically referring to the four years he is said to have retreated to the desert, where he purified his soul through physical suffering. Here, the bearded saint is half naked on bended knee before Christ on the cross, and through the scale of the cross and naturalistic features of His body, it is suggested that Jerome kneels before, not an icon as is more typically represented, but instead witnesses Christ's actual death. As it is written Saint Jerome was tormented by vivid hallucinations for which he would beat himself with a stone, (shown here clenched in his right hand) the sculptor may be suggesting through the life-like representation of Christ, one of Jerome's visions. Various attributes of Saint Jerome have been included within this simple composition; a cardinal's hat hanging on a broken tree branch refers to Jerome's translation of the Bible into Latin, while a heraldically stylised lion with raised paw recalls a fable in which Jerome pulls a thorn from its paw, and is repaid with the lion's unconditional devotion. A rocky ledge suggests the cave that served as Saint Jerome's desert shelter.

This fine marble relief of *The Penitent Saint Jerome* is the work of a highly proficient sculptor. Identified by a fusion of aesthetic maturity – as seen in the musculature of both Christ and Saint Jerome – with an overall simplicity of design,

Italian, Naples, *The Penitent St Jerome*, detail

24

[1] BENTLEY, 1987.
[2] ABBATE, 1992, fig. 36, 'Saint Jerome in the Desert'.
[3] ABBATE, 1992, chapter III. Conway Library illustration.
[4] VASARI, *Le Vite*, volume IV, p. 407.

RELATED LITERATURE:

ABBATE, F., *La Scultura Napoletana del Cinquecento*, Rome, 1992.
BENTLEY, J.H., *Politics and Culture in Renaissance Naples*, Princeton, NJ, 1987.
RYDER, A., *Alfonso the Magnanimous, King of Aragon, Naples and Sicily, 1396-1458*, Oxford and New York, 1990.

its style reflects artistic production by the turn of the 16th century in Naples. Exacerbated by the Spanish conquest and the subsequent end of Argonese rule in 1506, there emerged great urban expansion in keeping with the city of Naples' new status as a southern capital of the Hapsburg empire.[1] The effect was a collaboration between regional, northern and Spanish artists, resulting in a hybridisation of artistic currents that characterised the production of Naples throughout the 16th century and mirrored the cosmopolitan nature of its political rule and patronage. It is within this stylistic blend of technical accomplishment and archaizing reliance that Naples finds its zenith of artistic expression.

The present relief of *The Penitent Saint Jerome* is evidence of the finest Neapolitan production of this important period. Characterised by a methodical arrangement of compositional details, as seen in the heraldically stylised lion, or the painstakingly observed leaves of a gnarled tree coupled with an abstract treatment of chiselled rock, the present narrative typifies an aesthetic. This defining character can be seen in a relief of similar subject matter, by the early 16th century Neapolitan sculptor, Tommaso Malvito [fl 1484–1508], where he employs the same stylised lion, leafy trees with long, slender and knotted trunks, and suggests rocks in a comparatively abstract manner.[2] The characteristic use of large areas of empty, smooth marble finds parallel in numerous contemporary monuments in and around Naples; including a funerary altar to Saint Jerome, by the Donnorso Family in the cathedral of San Domenico Maggiore,[3] where the central relief depicts a similarly kneeling Saint Jerome, more relevantly occupying an identical shallow field, accented by a high relief foreground on a nearly flat surface.

Stylistically, this relief of *The Penitent Saint Jerome* is consistent with that of a sculptor working in Naples during the first quarter of the 16th century, Girolamo da Santacroce (1502-1537). Highly praised by Vasari,[4] Girolamo's many documented works are characterised by strong foreground compositions, set against large areas of smooth marble and accented by well-conceived figures and drapery comprised of thin, pasty folds. Girolamo da Santacroce's *Deposition* relief for San Annunziata, Naples, is significant in its technique of carving, clearly observed in the drilled strands of hair, anatomy of Christ and simplistic cross on a smooth plane, and providing a marked comparison to the present relief of *The Penitent Saint Jerome*. Distinct parallels in the handling of facial features and posture can be appreciated in the tilted head of Saint Jerome, looking up to the vision before him, and that of Joseph who supports the dead weight of Christ as He is taken from the cross. The minimalist outline of the cross in each relief, serves an intriguing and rarely seen compositional device, possibly idiosyncratic to Girolamo da Santacroce style.

5 BUST OF POMONA

Attributed to
ANTONIO MINELLO
[Padua, C. 1465 – C. 1529]

Terracotta and polychrome
34 x 37.6 cm ($13\frac{1}{4}$ x $14\frac{3}{4}$")

PROVENANCE:
Stefan Auspitz Collection, Vienna
Bondi Collection, Vienna
Figdor Collection, Vienna
Blumka, New York

EXHIBITED:
Victoria and Albert Museum, London
Earth and Fire: Italian Terracotta Sculpture from Donatello to Canova,
14 March-7 July 2002.

[1] PLANISCIG, L., *Venezianische Bildauer der Renaissance*, Vienna, 1921, figs 166, 167, pp. 155-173.

[2] Indeed the first mention of Antonio Minello was in a document of 1483 in relation to the Arca del Santo, and his specific involvement with the design and production of the choir screen.

[3] Kunsthistorisches Museum, Vienna, c. 1505/10

[4] Cappella del Santo, Padua, c. 1500-19, marble relief. A detail of a female figure from this relief displaying affinities useful to the present discussion is published as fig. 20 in SCHULZ, *Burlington Magazine*, 1995.

[5] V&A, London. *Mercury*, signed and dated 1527, marble [Height: 76.8 cm]

This bust was published for the first and only time by Leo Planiscig in 1921.[1] At that date, it was in the Stefan Auspitz Collection, Vienna, and Planiscig devoted considerable attention to it, illustrating it with two photographs. The work subsequently passed into the collections of Bondi, Figdor, and Blumka, establishing an illustrious pedigree. According to Planiscig, the work was by the mid-15th-century Padua sculptor, Giovanni Minello (c.1440-1528), and datable to the end of that century. However, Planiscig's dating is approximately a generation out, and the work has stronger affinities with the sculptural style of Minello's son, Antonio (c.1465-c.1529), who was also active in Padua during the first two decades of the 16th century.

This important terracotta bust of the Roman goddess of fruit, *Pomona*, corresponds both in its classicising subject matter and format, to a distinguished period of production characterised by the *all'antica* bust and the genius of various Venetian sculptors; including Tullio (1455-1532) and his brother Antonio Lombardo (1458-1516), as well as the enigmatic Simone Bianco (c.1510-c.1553). This style culminated in 1498 in the design and decoration of the Arca del Santo chapel in Padua, a project that drew the most celebrated Veneto sculptors of the day, including Antonio Minello.[2] That Planiscig's dating of the present bust ascribed it to Antonio's father, Giovanni Minello, is not unusual, for he studied with Tullio's father, Pietro Lombardo (1435-1515) in the 1460s, subsequently reflecting this earlier Lombardesque style; a style distinctly disseminated and gently modified by the time the sons of either master were working, but an evolution only recently understood.

Despite a stylistic relationship, extending to both subject and general format, between *Pomona* and various works known to be by the Lombardo brothers; for example Tullio's *Bacchus and Ariadne*,[3] or the reliefs by both sculptors for the Arca del Santo, ultimately the modelling of this bust displays a variation on this vernacular, and as the elder Minello specialised in decorative marble carving, his son, Antonio, recognised for his ability in handling the figurative, is a more likely candidate. The rather generalised classicism of the *Pomona* is very close to the morphology of Antonio's figures in his relief for the chapel in the Arca del Santo, the *Investiture of St Anthony as a Franciscan*,[4] completed in 1519, or his small marble figure of *Mercury*, now in the Victoria and Albert Museum, London.[5] This reinstated classicism was evocative of the period, and promoted by an intimate group of the most influential sculptors of the first half of the 16th century; a prevailing aesthetic that ultimately encouraged one of its most recognised proponents, Gianmaria Mosca (*circa* 1493-after 1574). As an early workshop

Fig.1, Antonio Minello, *Bust of a woman*, Museo Bardini, Florence

assistant to Antonio Minello, stylistic reverberations between Mosca and his mentor Minello are not surprising.[6]

It is only within the last ten years and the discoveries of further works attributed to Antonio Minello that his idiosyncratic style has become apparent.[7] The marble statuette of *Mercury* in the Victoria and Albert Museum is inscribed with Minello's name, the name of its patron, Marcantonio Michiel, and its precise term of execution, 14th February to 15th June 1527. Antonio probably died in September 1528, when plague was ravishing the Veneto, effectively marking this statuette as a late work. A consistency is apparent between this late statuette of *Mercury*, and figures within Minello's earlier relief, *Investiture of St Anthony as a Franciscan*, particularly with the head of the armed man, showing the same fleshy, parted lips, small forehead, and dimpled, raised chin. Identical comparisons can be made with the *Bust of a woman* in the Museo Bardini, Florence,[8] (fig 1) based without alteration on Minello's Padua *Saint Justine* carved for the façade of the Cappella del Santo, and naturally more in keeping with the present female portrait bust of *Pomona*.

By the mid 1520s the genre of the free-standing portrait bust- the appearance of which in Venetian sculpture was extraordinarily belated- had probably gained currency in Venice. Typically this tradition marks its genesis with Tullio Lombardo's double relief portrait in the Ca' d'Oro, Venice, while by the middle of the 16th century the promotion of the female bust is more commonly associated to an Aretine émigré, Simone Bianco, who was established as a master in the Veneto from at least 1512. While many similarly styled female busts are ascribed to Bianco,

[6] Refer, for example, to Mosca's marble relief of *Eurydice* [38.4 x 22.1 cm], in the Metropolitan Museum, New York.
[7] Refer to both mentioned articles by ANNE MARKHAM SCHULTZ, each dealing with important recent discoveries that have re-defined Antonio Minello's recognised style.
[8] This polychrome terracotta bust [95.5 cm] provides interesting technical comparisons to the present bust of *Pomona*. [Museo Bardini, Florence]

Fig. 2, Simone Bianco, *Bust of a Woman,* Staatliche Museen, Berlin

[9] Bianco, *Bust of a young woman*, marble, Staatliche Museen, Berlin. Illustrated as fig. 24 in SCHULTZ's *Burlington Magazine* article, 1995.

[10] This bust, published for the first time in 1995, has been in the possession of its present owners, Helen and Nereo Fioratti, since 1963, having previously belonged to Mrs Fioratti's mother, Countess Ruth Costantino of New York, who purchased it from the Roman dealer and collector, Morandotti. This *Bust of a young woman* is one of the two works by Antonio Minello discussed by SCHULZ, *Burlington Magazine*, 1995.

none are dated, and it is only from 1538 that literary sources attest his manufacture of such works. Nevertheless, it can be assumed with authority that Bianco's famous marble bust of a woman (fig 2), seemingly expiring with the anxiety of love, in the Staatliche Museen, Berlin-Dahlem[9] preceded and inspired Antonio Minello's redaction of this theme, as evidenced by the present bust of *Pomona*.

A recent discovery by Anne Markham Schulz of a previously unpublished marble *Bust of a young woman* in a private collection New York[10], makes a fascinating addition to the known works by Antonio Minello, and is further proof of the effect that Bianco's Berlin bust had on Minello's perception of the female portrait. Correspondences between Bianco's Berlin bust, and both that in New York and the present *Pomona* are undisputed, in fact Minello's choice of a loose fitting *camicia*, or pleated shirt, for *Pomona*, exposing the right shoulder and breast in exactly the same manner, may well have been a direct tribute to Bianco's mastery. Interestingly, Minello's *Bust of a young woman* in New York also wears a revealing pleated shirt, similarly exposing a single breast; probably meant as a sign of surrender to sexual desire, alternatively it can be used as a symbol of chastity, as in classical representations of the goddess Diana, or such heroines as Judith or Lucretia both of whom had virtuously survived the attentions of lustful men. According to Ovid's *Metamorphoses* [14.623-771] and the account of *Pomona*'s eventual submission to the persistent charms of Vertumnus, the Roman god of the changing seasons, it is more likely that Minello is suggesting *Pomona*'s sexual desire, the victory of her emphatic suitor, and finally the symbolic fertility associated with this earth goddess.

Beyond establishing a feasible chain of inspiration, comparing these three female portrait busts effectively helps in defining Antonio Minello's idiosyncratic aesthetic and carving technique; different from that of Simone Bianco, and certainly of the Lombardo brothers. Minello's marble *Bust of a young woman* in New York and that of *Pomona* provide a marked continuity in the treatment of similar subject matter, as can be noted in the regularity of their full facial features, broad, rounded shoulders, fleshy, parted lips and widely spaced breasts. Each of these components can be extracted from Minello's relief for the Arca del Santo chapel, and equally, in regards to the physiognomy, in his signed marble statuette of *Mercury*. An overall softness of form, avoidance of musculature, and finer details such as delineated pupils that occupy nearly the entire surface of the eye ball, can be uniformly observed on the works that comprise Antonio Minello's production; a regularity observed even in the present terracotta of *Pomona* where large, faint circles are scratched into each eye, probably before the clay hardened, to suggest pupils.

The fictive bronze surface of this bust of *Pomona* is remarkable, as it is probably the earliest to have survived. Various contemporary terracotta reliefs in the church of the Eremitani in Padua are treated in the same way, varnished to resemble bronze, and we know that this was a standard practice through the start of the 17th century. The present design is far too fussy to have been executed in bronze and its scale (34 x 37.6 cm) would have made a bronze cast prohibitively expensive to all but the richest collectors. In her book, *The Scholar in his Study*, Dora Thornton quotes from a description of the 16th-century connoisseur, Fra Sabba da Castiglione's studio contents, in which he makes specific mention of "...a figure of Saint Jerome, made of terracotta but finished so as to imitate bronze..." The mentioned work is now in the Kunsthistorisches Museum, Vienna, but its surface, sadly in keeping with many works of art of the period, was later stripped, probably sometime in the 19th century. Such fictive bronzes were commonly employed as cheaper decorative devices on shelves and cabinets as can be seen in the paintings of Carpaccio, and this is the likely context for which the Pomona was made.

PAINT ANALYSIS

Original paint layer over terracotta with remnants of an exceedingly rare mosaic gold pigment. Results of paint analysis available on request, as is a thermoluminescence report.

PUBLISHED:

BOUCHER, B., ED., *Earth and Fire: Italian Terracotta Sculpture from Donatello to Canova*, exhibition catalogue, Yale University Press, 2001,
Houston Museum of Fine Arts, 18 November 2001 –3 February 2002.
Victoria and Albert Museum, London, 14 March 2002-7 July 2002. pp. 23, fig. 23
PLANISCIG, L., *Venezianische Bildhauer der Renaissance*, Vienna, 1921, figs 166, 167, pp. 155-173.

RELATED LITERATURE:

LUCHS, A., *Tullio Lombardo and ideal portrait sculpture in Renaissance Venice, 1490-1530*, Cambridge, 1995.
RIGONI, E., 'Giovanni Minello e la cappella dell'Arca di S Antonio', *Atti & Mem. Accad. Patavina Sci., Lett. & A.*, xlv (1953-4), pp. 90-96; also in *L'arte rinascimentale in Padova: Studi e documenti, med. & uman.*, ix (Padua, 1970), pp. 259-64
SCHULZ, A., 'Four New Works by Antonio Minello', *Mitteilungen des Kunsthistorischen Institutes in Florenz*, xxxi , 1987, pp. 291-326.
SCHULZ, A., 'Two New Works by Antonio Minello', *Burlington Magazine*, cxxxvii, December 1995, pp. 799-808.
THORNTON, D., *The Scholar in his Study; ownership and experience in Renaissance Italy*, New Haven, 1998.

6 INCENSE BURNER

Attributed to
DESIDERIO DA FIRENZE
[active Padua, 1532-1545]

Circa 1540
Bronze
51.2 cm (20$\frac{1}{4}$")

PROVENANCE:
Sir Julius Wernher, 1st Bt. (1850-1912),
Red Room, Bath House, London.
Alice, Lady Wernher (1862-1945),
his widow (later Lady Ludlow).
Sir Harold Wernher (1893-1973), their son;
at Luton Hoo, Bedfordshire, from 1948.

EXHIBITED:
Donatello e il suo tempo. Il bronzetto
a Padova nel Quattrocento e nel Cinquecento,
Musei Civici, Padua, 8 April-15 July 2001, p. 183, no. 43.

[1] Riccio's *Paschal Candlestick* is regarded as his masterpiece, and was commissioned for the Santo in Padua, and completed in 1516. These enormous candlesticks (3.92 m) remain *in situ* and are as convoluted a decorative scheme as that of the present incense burner, certainly influenced by these earlier and undoubtedly well-known candlesticks. Interestingly, as a definitively ecclesiastical commission, Riccio made no effort to bridle his overtly pagan designs for which he was famous, and as curiously, the Church appears to have had no reservations.

[2] WARREN, J., "The Faun Who Plays on the Pipes": A New Attribution to Desiderio da Firenze, in *Small Bronzes in the Renaissance*, ed. PINCUS, D., Trustees of the National Gallery of Art, Washington, 2001, pp.83-103.

Of the four known examples of this elaborate incense burner model, the present cast is the finest. With minor variations between them, two are today in the Metropolitan Museum, New York, and belong to the Lehman Collection, while the other, from the Widener Collection, is in the National Gallery, Washington. (fig. 1) Of the two Lehman examples, one is markedly inferior to the other, and may be a later cast. Long-associated with the master of pagan design, Andrea Riccio [Padua, 1470-1532], on account of their shared decorative vernacular with Riccio's great Paschal Candelabrum,[1] *closer examination of individual elements, anatomy type and surface finishing reveals an argument for a different authorship entirely, simultaneously focusing the defines of Riccio's production while clarifying the subsequent importance of Desiderio da Firenze.*

This fascinating cylindrical bronze incense burner plays an imperative role within the ongoing study of the enigmatic sculptor, Desiderio da Firenze, and his idiosyncratic yet derivative style. As part of a larger group of known models, including *Pan Listening to Echo*, in the Ashmolean Museum, Oxford; variations on the *Kneeling Satyr*, an example of which is in a private collection in New York (fig 2); and a standing figure of *Mercury* known in three versions, one of which is in the Staatliche Museen, Berlin, the Wernher *Incense Burner* effectively contributes to both the aesthetic and technical continuity of what is emerging as a congruous addition to the production of Desiderio da Firenze.

Fig. 1, *Incense Burner,* Widener Collection, National Gallery, Washington, D.C.

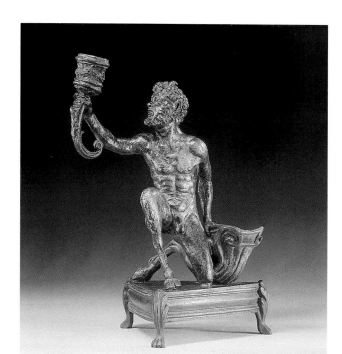

Fig. 2, *Kneeling Satyr,* Private Collection, New York

Convincingly deciphered in a recently published article by Jeremy Warren,[2] this persistently curious group of Paduan bronzes dated to the second quarter of the 16th century can now be regarded as a homogenous group; a group possessing unarguable decorative and stylistic responses to Riccio, while characterised by disparate casting technique, and a range of quality and finishing. The relationship between the present *Incense Burner* and the group of models discussed in Warren's article is not newly recognised, and even as early as Planiscig's 1927 argument for Riccio,[3] he separated the kneeling and seated satyrs and the satyr that surmounts the present *Incense Burner* as occupying a slightly digressional aspect of Riccio's production, although still categorically ascribing these works to him. It was not again until 1997 and Anthony Radcliffe's reassessment of Riccio's long accepted oeuvre, that this related group was resuscitated and concluded as encompassing a definitively independent group of bronzes that "must have been the products of a skilled and prolific Paduan workshop that, after the death of Riccio in 1532, exploited the superficialities of his imagery, possibly over a considerable period of time."[4] Acknowledging an earlier and unsubstantiated suggestion of Desiderio da Firenze for the triangular incense burner model [one of which is in the Metropolitan Museum] as feasible, Radcliffe summarises that Desiderio may in fact be "a prime candidate" for the authorship of the group of seated satyrs that form part of the group of which the present *Incense Burner* is a part.

Radcliffe's earlier study,[5] specifically on that of the impressive sphinx andirons in the Victoria and Albert Museum (fig. 3), substantiates later analyses that work to disentangle the Riccio attribution in favour of Desiderio da Firenze. Long

[3] PLANISCIG, L., 1927, pp.346-350.
[4] RADCLIFFE, 1997, p.91.
[5] RADCLIFFE, 1982, p.418.
[6] Museo Civico, Padua. Commissioned by the Maggior Consiglio of the Comune of Padua, payments to Desiderio are documented from 1532-3. This urn is considered to be one of the most technical proficiently poured bronzes of the 16th century.

accepted as being the work of Riccio, Radcliffe compares the bases on these andirons with distinct satyr masks to the *Voting Urn* of the Great Council of the Commune of Padua and its analogous decorative complexes.[6] Regarded as a definitive work by Desiderio da Firenze himself, based on conclusive documented evidence, the *Voting Urn* must serve as the stylistic and technical touchstone for subsequent attributions. Importantly, Radcliffe's argument for Desiderio, in regards to the Victoria and Albert sphinx andirons furthers Warren's subsequent ascription in regards to the Metropolitan Museum triangular incense burner model, as this specific design, of which various other examples exist, incorporates three markedly similar winged sphinx (fig. 3).

The same series of satyr masks that decorate both the upper and lower bowls of the *Voting Urn* used to help reconsider the Victoria and Albert Museum's sphinx andirons, are even closer related to those that adorn the sides of the present *Incense Burner.* Intermittently spaced around the central and lower register, their fantastical faces would have promised dramatic effect when in use, as swirls of perfumed smoke would have issued from their pierced, open mouths. Further grotesque masks, wrapped in coiled snakes and with wild hair suggestive of Medusa, decorate the cover, perforated in the same way. Moreover, the winged putti that nearly crouch beneath the lip of the cover, appearing to support its weight, are paralleled in character and type to those on the *Voting Urn.* Additionally, the larger masks of the *Voting Urn* bear close comparison to the fabulous feet designed as elongated satyr masks, that support the triangular

Fig. 4, *Incense Burner,* Metropolitan Museum, New York

perfume burner in the Metropolitan Museum, an equally elaborate design as that of the present Wernher example and probably conceived around the same time.

[7] WARREN, 2001, pp.83-103.

The technical virtuosity of the present *Incense Burner* is apparent, and offers sufficient deviation from Riccio's characteristic surface handling to further the argument for Desiderio's authorship. Inspection of his autograph bronzes, for example the *Shouting Horseman* or the *Satyr and Satyress*, both in the Victoria and Albert Museum, reveals Riccio's fascination with surface detailing; a fastidiousness in overall filing and hammering that can only be reminiscent of a bronze sculptor trained as a goldsmith, as was Riccio. While Desiderio appears to possess the same bravura for original wax modelling, the accuracy of his eventual cast permits a near avoidance of surface refinement, and characterises, amongst others, the *Pan Listening to Echo*, variant types of the *Kneeling Satyr* model ultimately derived from Severo da Ravenna, and the present *Incense Burner*, all part of the decidedly homogenous group analysed by Warren.[7]

Riccio's resounding association with the grotesque, fantastical world of paganism may well attribute to unfounded, earlier attributions to his production, and it is through such deeper, technical analysis that variations within this world materialize. The myriad of pagan and mythological features that epitomize the present *Incense Burner* can be individually analysed and find comparative sources among various aspects of the recognised group discussed by Warren. The satyr holding pan-pipes that surmounts the present cylindrical *Incense Burner* bears an interesting continuity with the *Pan listening to Echo* in the Ashmolean Museum,

[8] The second documented work of Desiderio da Firenze, and one of which the exact detail of his involvement remains a mystery, although it is known for certain that he was specifically recommended for the commission by Pietro Bembo.

PUBLISHED:

1913 Bath House Inventory, no. 48, p.10, in the Red Room, on the mantelpiece.
1914 Wernher Inventory, no. 41, p.10.
BODE, WILHELM VON, *The Italian Bronze Statuettes of the Renaissance*, rev. ed by JAMES DAVID DRAPER, New York, 1980, p. 93 pl. LX.

RELATED LITERATURE:

CARRINGTON, J.E., "A New Look at Desiderio da Firenze and the Paduan Voting Urn", *Bollettino del Museo Civico di Padova*, 73, 1984, p.109.
PLANISCIG, L., *Andrea Riccio*, Vienna, 1927.
RADCLIFFE, A., "Ricciana", *Burlington Magazine*, 124, July 1982, 412-424.
RADCLIFFE, A., "The Debasement of Images: The Sculptor Andrea Riccio and the Applied Arts in Padua in the Sixteenth Century", in *The Sculpted Object 1400-1700*, EDS. CURRIE, S. AND MOTTURE, P., Aldershot, Hants, England, 1997.
WARREN, J., "The Faun Who Plays on the Pipes": A New Attribution to Desiderio da Firenze, in *Small Bronzes in the Renaissance*, ed. PINCUS, D., Trustees of the National Gallery of Art, Washington, 2001.

We owe this attribution to the thorough research of Anthony Radcliffe and Jeremy Warren. The contents of the present catalogue entry is reliant on Warren's paper presented to the symposium held at the National Gallery of Art, Washington, entitled 'Small Bronzes in the Renaissance'.

Oxford, as both are characterised with a minimum of surface hammering, similar torso anatomy marked by broad shoulders, and sensitive physiognomy, decidedly less bestial than those that characterise Riccio's *Satyr and Satyress* for example. Furthermore, the schematic decorative devices ultimately derived from Riccio's *Paschal Candelabrum*, of shells and foliate swags, that populate the drum socle upon which the Oxford *Pan* sits, are like those on the narrow, lower register of the present *Incense Burner*, and equally on the incense burner with triangular-shaped base in the Metropolitan Museum, New York. (fig.4)

Through information preserved in one of only two surviving documents relating to Desiderio da Firenze's career, we learn of his involvement with the Paduan sculptor, Tiziano Minio [c.1511-1552] on the bronze cover for the baptismal font for Saint Mark's, Venice, contracted in April 1545.[8] As Minio's style appears to have permeated various aspects of Desiderio's production, for example the male nude figures that emerge from the sides of the present *Incense Burner*, it may be that the pair of sculptors were commissioned to work together often, and Minio's style disseminated, like that of Severo da Ravenna and Riccio, through the growing number of works attributed to Desiderio da Firenze. If the group of bronze models analysed most recently by Warren, including the present *Incense Burner*, are in fact by Desiderio da Firenze, he would have been responsible for one of the most productive workshops in Northern Italy during the second quarter of the 16th century, perhaps on a par with that of Severo da Ravenna. In respect to the many years of Desiderio's career that we know nothing about, we must assume that the derivative nature of the designs attributed to his name were in direct response to the market demand; a demand which would naturally have heightened following Riccio's death, and a market to which Desiderio responded with the highest level of technical proficiency, marked by a minimum of afterwork and a magnificent compendium of decorative devices imbued with idiosyncratic refinement.

7 OIL LAMP IN THE FORM OF AN ACROBAT

ITALY, PADUA
[Early 16th Century]

Bronze
Height 14.5 cm (5¾")

PROVENANCE:
Paris, art market 1913
(L. PLANISCIG, *Andrea Riccio*,
Vienna, 1927, pp. 180-82, pl. 200);

Private collection, Basel
(L. PLANISCIG,
Piccoli Bronzi Italiani del Rinascimento,
Milan, 1930, pl. LXXVII, p. 19).

This amusingly obscene oil-lamp shows a contortionist, bent double while thrusting his head between his legs, which he holds up taut in mid-air with both hands. He is meant to be defaecating into a pan (half an oval in shape and decorated below with an acanthus leaf) that protrudes organically from his rear, out of which the wick of the lamp would have protruded suggestively, when lit it would have illuminated grotesquely.

The number of examples of this particular model that are now in circulation gives a misleading impression of its rarity, for many are deliberate variants or simply derivatives of inferior quality, produced when the best examples were still believed to date from Roman times, and antiquities were all the rage with collectors and scholars in the period of the Grand Tour. There are two principal varieties: those that are designed to hang from a loop cast with – or brazed on to – the soles of the raised feet; and those which have a small, spreading foot in the shape of a rosette cast into the middle of their backs, to enable them to stand.

One that appeared at Sotheby's, London, 7 December 1989, lot 72, which had a beard and eyes inlaid with silver, on account of which it was mistakenly hailed as Mantuan in origin, is the best of the former type, while a close runner-up was another (lacking the loop, but with holes in its feet for one), sold at Christie's, London, 7 July 1992, lot 153. Its face was not bearded, but similar to the one under discussion. The present lamp is the finest of the second category. Both categories contain one or two items of top quality. It seems therefore that both were authentic models with alternative means of support, rather than one being derived from the other.

While the lamp does balance perfectly on its integrally cast foot, for safety's sake it would need to have been mounted more securely. It probably did not belong on the eagle's-claw stand with which it was illustrated in Planiscig (1927): had it done so, this would have provided evidence corroborating a possible attribution to Severo Calzetta of Ravenna, in whose workshop such claw feet were commonly screwed on to a variety of other bronze artefacts. An engraving in the treatise on classical lamps by Liceto that shows a lamp like ours fortunately includes a tripod base ornamented with grotesque masks that is obviously of 16th century rather than ancient manufacture, and this indicates the proper form of mounting, though none survives.

The question of authorship remains to be satisfactorily determined by modern criteria. At the time when this type of lamp was segregated from antique examples, the only immediately available candidate was the main sculptor of the Paduan school, Andrea Briosco, called Il Riccio, so that – as has been noted – von Bode and Planiscig opted for him. Planiscig (1930) even surmised that Il Riccio may have been making fun of his own appearance, for the curly hair after which he was given his nickname, seems from various self-portraits to have been that characteristic of a black man, with facial features to match: *L'acrobata Lucerna che esegue le sue contorsioni ginnastiche… è un modello molte volte variato a differamente combinato; l'esemplare qui riprodotto è certamente un originale uscito dalle mani del Maestro, che pare abbia voluto caratterizzare umoristicamente sé medesimo nella faccia del negro dal naso piatto, dagli zigomi sporgenti e dalla chioma ricciuta.*

The relatively recent emergence from obscurity of Severo Calzetta of Ravenna (1465/75-1538), whose best work – and even workshop productions – previously had been subsumed into that of Il Riccio (see Planiscig's monograph of 1927), provides a viable, alternative candidate, though – in the event – his claims do not seem as strong as those of Riccio himself[1].

The oil-lamp is one of a whole class of functional, household bronzes that were produced as reproduction or substitute ancient Roman artefacts, derived from surviving authentic examples, but frequently, as here, "improved on" by Renaissance sculptors, possibly egged on by their learned patrons, the humanists of Padua University (for whom the comedies of Aristophanes or the *Satires* of Juvenal provided intriguing examples of very bawdy, often anal-obsessive, ancient humour). Their sometimes rough surfaces and dark patina may have been designed to replicate those of antiquities that had been buried for centuries and had become corroded and encrusted. It is not known if they were recognized in the first instance as contemporary, rather than ancient, bronzes, and purchased as such at fair prices, or if they were forgeries made deliberately to deceive, perhaps being provided with false but convincing provenances by disingenuous scholars to help in marketing them to eager collectors, who had few standards of comparison. An example still in Ferrara was correctly listed in an inventory taken in 1584 of statues, etc., belonging to Duke Alfonso II d'Este, as "believed to be modern" (*lanterna as use di un bambozzo con la testa fra le gambe, si crede sia moderna*).

However, by under a century later, they were evidently accepted as *bona fide* Montfaucon. As Bliss (1995) writes, in translation: "Understandably enraptured, Licetus, under a chapter heading entitled appropriately "Concerning the Amusing, although Indecent Lamp of Pighetti", devotes a full nine columns of attendant text pertaining to this sole contortionist. His discourse states in part: "A friend who considered his lamps deserving of attention brought me a drawing of his which

[1] Arguments for Il Riccio include discussions of physiognomic comparisons with elements from the Paschal candlestick in The Santo, Padua and the facial type of the group of sea monsters and Satyrs by Il Riccio. This comparison was reiterated independently by J. Bilss in his article when he republished the oil lamp with silver eyes sold at Sotheby's and states "only one other example of remarkably high merit, in a private collection in Basel, is likewise worthy of being considered an autograph work of Riccio himself, as initially established by Planiscig" – Referring to our piece.

[2] Further illustrations of the oil lamp can be found in a drawing by Fragonard (1732-1806) where he shows the Bargello version on a sheet of sketches made in 1761 and labelled in his own hand "Bronzes antiques Gallerie du Grand Duc á Florence". Only a decade later Johann Zoffany (1733-1810) included the Medici lamp in the foreground of his celebrated depiction, commissioned by Queen Charlotte in 1772, of the Tribuna of the Uffizi Gallery.

RELATED LITERATURE:

(*as an antiquity*)
LICETO, F., *De Lucernis Antiquorum Reconditis,* Udine, 1652 (Padua, 1662), Book VI, Chapter 74, columns 966-74
DE WILDE, M., *Signa antiqua a Museo J. de Wilde,* 1703, pl. 16); *Collezione di tune le antichita che si conservano nel Museo Naniano di Venezia,* Venice, 1815, no. 39
DE MONTFAUCON, B., *L'Antiquate Expliquee et representee en figures,* Paris, 1719, V, II, pl. 152,4 (variant with a beard, belonging to Monsieur Foucault).
(*as a Renaissance artefact*)
VON BODE, W. (ED. J. DRAPER), *Italian Bronze Statuettes of the Renaissance,* New York, 1980, pl. XLVII (suspect example with clothes and boots on, Prince

Trivulzio, Milan, c. 1908)
PLANISCIG, L., *Andrea Riccio*, Vienna, 1927, pp. 180-82, pls. 200, 202-3 (present cast and another similar, R. Berl, Vienna, a third, probably later, French variant, Bibliotheque Nationale, Paris; a fourth, Museo Civico Industriale, Turin; a fifth, Barsanti Collection, Rome)
VON BODE, W., *Die Italienische Bild-werke...II, Bronzestatuetten*, Berlin, 1930, pp. 16-17, no. 71, pl. 27 (a cast in the Staatliche Museen, Berlin, described by Bode as "excellent, possibly an autograph piece" by Il Riccio);
MONTAGU, J., *Bronzes,* London, 1963, pl. 2 (example in Museo Nazionale del Bargello, Florence)
MARIACHER, G., *Bronzetti Yeneti del Rinascimento*, Vicenza, 1971/93, pp. 29-30, no. 79 (example in Museo Nazionale del Bargello, Florence; listing also the present cast, when in Basel, and one of inferior quality in the Museo Comer, Venice)
CALLMANN, E., *Beyond Nobility: Art for the Private Citizen in the early Renaissance,* exh. cat., Allentown Art Museum, 1981, no. 62 .(with Blumka Gallery, New York: bearded acrobat, hanging from a chain)
MATTHIESEN FINS ART LTD., *From Borso to Cesare d'Este : The School of Ferrara 1450-1628,* exh. cat., London, 1984, no. 90 (unbearded man, with loop for suspension, from the old ducal collections, since 1584, Museo Estense, Ferrara)
LIEBIEGHAUS MUSEUM ALTER PLASTIK, *Natur and Antike in der Renaissance,* exh. cat., Frankfurt-am-Main, 1986, no. 221 (indifferent cast with an integral loop for suspension, then with E. Lubin, New York)
BLISS, J., "A renaissance acrobat lamp by Andrea Riccio:its mistaken history as an ancient bronze", in *Source: Notes in the History of Art* (Columbia University, New York), XIV, 3, 1995, pp. 15-20.

provokes laughter, along with the bronze lamp itself from the collection of the eminent Jacopo Pighetti, a city-father of Bergamo... The lamp is of bronze, represents a nude human body, the head endowed with curly hair compressed between the two shins raised up high, with both feet raised up in the air... bent over and with a mighty effort he seems to be striving to deposit faeces from his bowel into a basin which juts out, it has the illuminating flame customary in a lamp... It is unsure whether the figure represents an Ethiopian man, or a woman; for there is not displayed any sign of any kind of sex, neither of visible male organs, nor of a female private part. The short curly hair does not necessarily prove masculinity, for female Moors are similarly short and curly-haired, inasmuch as they are people of torrid regions'." Evidently Licetus was confronted with an example like the present one, which is sex-less, though the Sotheby's example and several others have clearly defined male organs.

Bernard de Montfaucon (1655-1741), the French antiquarian, alongside his illustration of one of the hanging type, excuses the rude subjects of this and three other Paduan lamps on his plate as follows: "The three following lamps on this plate... seem made to shew either what the workman, or he who commanded the work, could possibly imagine most odd and extravagant, and do not want any further explanation"[2]

8 CHRIST THE REDEEMER

GIOVANNI DELLA ROBBIA
[Florence, 1449-1529/30]

Circa 1520-1525
Terracotta bust
55 x 53 x 24 cm (22 x 20 x 9½")

PROVENANCE:
Della Robbia family,
by descent to Marchesi Viviani della Robbia, Settignano.
Raoul Tolentino, Rome (his sale New York, 1920).

*Partially glazed, modelled in the round,
the walls with an even thickness of c. 3cm. throughout;
hair and garments glazed in mauve, yellow, blue and green,
traces of cold-painted polychromy in the recesses of the face.
A hole at the crown of the head, bored before firing,
intended for the insertion of a halo in either wood or metal*

[1] Dated circa 1483, this portrait of Christ, stimulated by the devotion of Savonarola, became the archetype from which other great artists drew, as the present work illustrates.

[2] Victoria and Albert Museum, inv. 476.67. Also refer to a related pigmented bust by the same artist in the Museo Civico, Pistoia.

This portrait of Christ *follows a standard iconographic type characteristic of Florentine sculpture of the Renaissance. Possessing an ethereal solemnity, the Redeemer stares straight ahead with only the slightest expression on his parted lips, distinctly recalling Verrocchio's* Christ *in his impressive bronze group of the* Incredulity of Thomas *at Orsanmichele in Florence.[1] Judged by contemporaries to be "the most beautiful head of the Saviour which has yet been made", Verrocchio's image of Christ prompted a vernacular that pervaded the times, epitomized through many unglazed terracotta busts, in particular those by Agnolo di Polo, for instance one in the Victoria and Albert Museum.[2] (fig 1) This, and other innumerable typological comparisons only serve to illuminate the rarity of the present example, conceived on its own and covered in brightly coloured realistic glaze.*

Fig. 2, Agnolo di Polo, *Bust of Christ*, Victoria and Albert Museum, London (©copyright V&A Picture Library)

No other versions of this bust are recorded, and the deep undercutting of the hair, sensitive modelling of the mouth and flowing ringlets of the beard exclude the possibility that the present work is a cast. The actual structure of the bust,[3] specific palette of the glazes[4] and the technique of cold painting the areas of exposed skin all conform to the accepted practice of the Della Robbia workshop.

The present bust is well known to Della Robbia experts, who from as early as 1897 have favoured an attribution to Giovanni.[5] Marquand, in his essential monograph on the dynasty of the della Robbias, gathered these earlier estimations, and secured this portrait of *Christ the Redeemer* to Giovanni, assigning its date of production to the first half of the 1520s, on the basis of its stylistic and technical relationship with a contemporaneous, clearly documented, commission at the Certosa del Galluzzo in Florence; which included Giovanni sculpting sixty-six medallions of prophets, apostles and saints, to be set in the spandrels of the arcade which surrounds the large cloister of this Carthusian monastery. The scale of this project leaves an iconographic repertory that is imperative when assessing works by Giovanni. One of these mentioned medallions shows a bust of Christ (fig. 2) bearing explicit affinities in both physiognomy and style to that of the present *Christ the Redeemer*.[6]

More recent study by Giancarlo Gentilini[7] includes the present bust, acknowledging its accepted ascription to Giovanni and concluding, through further comparative material in support, that the *Christ the Redeemer* is in fact an

[3] Typical to this Della Robbia type, the bust is made of distinctively fine, compact and plastic clay that when fired assumes a pallid, powder-like colouring.
[4] Specifically the porphyry mauve of the robe, and the deep yellow of the border, suggesting gold embroidery.
[5] For example: REYMOND, M., 1897, p.269./ BURLAMACCHI, 1900, pp.60/ CRUTTWELL, 1902, pp.234.
[6] Refer to a small illustration of this particular medallion of Christ, along with others of the group at Certosa, in MARQUAND, 1972, p.171.
[7] The present catalogue entry is largely based on the work Gentilini compiled on the present piece for its inclusion in his book; GENTILINI, 1992.
[8] Refer to sale catalogue: The American Art Association, *De luxe catalogue of the private collection of connoisseur Signor Raoul Tolentino*, ed. S de Ricci, New York, 1920, no.794 illustrated.

RELATED LITERATURE:

BURLAMACCHI, L., *Luca Della Robbia*, London, 1900.

Fig. 3, Giovanni Della Robbia, *Bust of Christ,* medallion, Certosa del Galluzzo, Florence

CRUTTWELL, M., *Luca and Andrea della Robbia and their successors*, London/New York, 1902.

GENTILINI, G., *I Della Robbia. La scultura invetriata nel Rinascimento*, Florence- n.d., 1992.

GENTILINI, G., ED., *I Della Robbia e l'arte nuova della scultura invetriata*, exhibition catalogue, Fiesole, 1998.

MARQUAND, A., *Luca della Robbia*, Princeton 1914 and New York, 1972.

REYMOND, M., *Les Della Robbia*, Florence, 1897.

PUBLISHED:

BURLAMACCHI, L., *Luca della Robbia*, London, 1900, pp.60, fig. 109.

CRUTTWELL, M., *Luca and Andrea della Robbia and their successors*, London/New York, 1902, pp.234, no. 1330.

GENTILINI, G., *I Della Robbia. La scultura invetriata nel Rinascimento*, Florence- n.d., 1992.

MARQUAND, 1972, p.133, item 134. Then in the Tolentino Sale of 1920.

REYMOND, M., *Les Della Robbia*, Florence, 1897, p.269.

This catalogue entry is based on the thorough research paper on this bust by Dr Giancarlo Gentilini, Florence

autograph work by Giovanni della Robbia, as its superior quality distinguishes it irrefutably from workshop production.

Beyond the credence of stylistic analyses, this bust of Christ the Redeemer boasts an esteemed provenance, placing it until the end of the last century in the collection of the Marchesi Viviani Della Robbia, the only descendants in Italy of this celebrated family of artists. From the family collection, the bust passed to the noted Roman antique dealer Raoul Tolentino, and was then part of his subsequent estate sale[8] held in New York in 1920.

9 A Rivergod

GIOVANNI FRANCESCO RUSTICI
[Florence 1474-1554 Tours]

Terracotta
First quarter 16th century
32 x 31.5 cm (12½ x 12⅓ ")

The present figure corresponds to Roman prototypes of Rivergods *utilised since the Middle Ages[1], while stylistically recalling, in pose and character, the images of nudes and semi-nudes which became an integral part of the vocabulary of the Italian Renaissance, a vernacular created through the works of Michelangelo, and immortalised in paint on the ceiling frescos of the Sistine chapel [1508-10] and in marble with the indomitable figure of* Giorno *in the Medici chapel of San Lorenzo in Florence [1526-34]. Michelangelo also intended four actual* Rivergods *to lie on the ground in front of the tomb of the Medici Captains for one of which a full-size terracotta model survives in the Casa Buonarotti, Florence.*

This emotive figure of a *Rivergod* represents a significant addition to a stylistically coherent group of terracottas that, initiated by Planiscig,[2] were for a long time ascribed to Jacopo Sansovino. Each figure within this group, representing *Rivergods* or *Bacchic figures* (fig 1), is modelled with similar authority; encompassing powerfully muscled men with similarly rugged features beneath unruly curls of hair, drooping moustaches and full beards.[3] Each of the group is shown holding an attribute, including a cornucopia, a ewer or a wine barrel, and incorporates swathes of boldly creased drapery that wrap around spiralling poses and cling to extended limbs.

The congruity of this group of figures, of which the present *Rivergod* is an indisputable part, is not in question, though it was not until 1991 and Boucher's study that they have together been reattributed to Rustici on the basis of their interdependence with Florentine sculpture of the first half of the 16th century. Boucher's ascription hinges upon fascinating correlations, both stylistic and technical, between this particular group in question and two early 16th century

[1] For example the *River Tiber* from the Vatican Belvedere, [now in the Louvre, Paris].
[2] PLANISCIG, L., 1921, pp. 372-74, figs. 392-93.
[3] This group consists of the following figures and now includes the present *Rivergod*: *Bacchic Figure,* Detroit Institute of Arts [no. 45.25]; *Rivergod,* Museum of Art, Providence, Rhode Island School of Design; *Bacchic figure,* Bayerisches Nationalmuseum, Munich; *Rivergod,* Badisches Landesmuseum, Karlsruhe [inv. 60/95]; *Bacchic figure* and *Rivergod,* publ. Weihrauch, 1965, pp. 266-67, in private collections.

Fig. 1, *Bacchic Figure,* The Detroit Institute of Arts, Michigan

Florentine works in the same medium; the celebrated *Battle Scenes* (fig 2) inspired by Leonardo's *Battle at Anghiari* fresco, and the terracottas ascribed to the anonymous 'Master of the Unruly Children'.[4]

The referred *Battle Scenes* are six in total,[5] and together they share remarkable affinities with the group of *Rivergods* and *Bacchic figures* to which the present figure is a part. Conceived on a similar scale, both groups correspond neatly in terms of form and movement, and finally, they all rise from an integral base specifically modelled as cleft rocks aligned in idiosyncratic pattern. Initially believed to be by Leonardo da Vinci[6] on account of their relationship with various known drawings including those for his Sforza and Trivulzio monuments, the *Battle Scenes* were more thoroughly analysed by Loeser in 1928 as being in fact works specifically described by Vasari as belonging to Leonardo's contemporary and close friend, Gian Francesco Rustici.[7]

Later, in 1981, Avery connected this same group of *Rivergods* and *Battle Scenes* with that of a distinguished group of terracottas representing the *Virgin and Child* and ascribed to an anonymous hand.[8] Boucher has since proposed them as being by Rustici.[9] Documented by Vasari as compositions reminiscent of Madonnas by Verrocchio, Rustici's first teacher, we are effectively presented with a phase of Rustici's production earlier than those that reflect more overt impressions of Leonardo da Vinci, his friend and collaborator, as seen in the mentioned *Battle Scenes*.

The three groups of terracottas, previously regarded as disparate, manifest the same hand and reveal the sculptor's tendency to produce a series of variations on

[4] This connection was first noted by Avery in AVERY/LAING, 1981, pp. 48-9. These pages show a comprehensive train of thought in the argument of these works as relations to Rustici.
[5] The known versions are: Collection Sheremetev; The Hermitage, St. Petersburg; Donazione Loeser, Palazzo della Signoria, Florence; Collection B.P. Johnson, Christie's, London, 17/4/1988, lot 86.
[6] Refer STITES, R.S., 1926 and 1931.
[7] " Gianfrancesco was taught many things by Leonardo", writes Vasari,, "...and to his pupils he gave many works of his hand such as drawings and models, and compositions in relief..." This would explain Rustici's allusions to Leonardo's impressive drawings. Vasari goes on to explain, "...His (Rustici's) horses, in terracotta, with men astride them, and others under their hoofs (BattleScenes), are many in the houses of the Florentine nobles. As he was thoroughly noble himself, and not avaricious and common like so many artists, he usually gave these works as presents to his friends..." [VASARI, 1881 ed, pp.601 & 608] This would explain why various models of these *Battle*

Scenes have such distinguished Florentine provenances; for example, Palazzo Rucellai and the Casa Ridolfi [Via Maggio].

[8] Refer AVERY/LAING, pp. 46-49. Includes illustrations of each of the three groups of terracottas being discussed here in relation to the present *Rivergod*.

[9] BOUCHER, 1991, II, pp. 341 ff.

[10] Placed over the north portal of the Florence Baptistry.

RELATED LITERATURE:

AVERY, C. & LAING, A., *Fingerprints of the Artists, European Terra-Cotta Sculpture from the Arthur M. Sackler Collections*, Washington DC 1981.

BOUCHER, B., *The Sculpture of Jacopo Sansovino*, 2 vols., London 1991.

PLANISCIG, L, *Venezianische Bildhauer der Renaissance*, Vienna 1921.

STITES, R.S., 'Leonardo da Vinci Sculptor', *Art Studies*, IV, 1926 and VIII, 1931.

A thermoluminescence test by the Oxford Institute of Archaeology has been obtained [copies available on request].

a particular theme, for commercial reasons. They are clearly not sketch models, but finished compositions made for collectors.

Rustici's most significant work, indeed the focus of his oeuvre, is a group of large bronze figures representing *St. John the Baptist Preaching to a Pharisee* and a *Levite* in Florence.[10] Accepting the obvious disparities of size and medium, this bronze group affirms the inclusion of the present terracotta *Rivergod* and its group, along with those of the *Battle Scenes* as works by Rustici. All employ the same deeply undercut drapery folds, thick muscular arms and unusually large hands. Moreover the tousled hair and beard of the bronze *Pharisee*, and the emotive expression behind deep-set eyes recall the associated terracottas. Also in the same impressive bronze group in Florence, we see an immediate correlation with the spiralling movement of the *Levite* so distinctive to the present *Rivergod*.

Effectively, this well documented bronze group of *St. John the Baptist Preaching*, commissioned in 1506, cast in 1509 and finally installed over the portal of the Florence Baptistry in 1511, helps in dating the present terracotta *Rivergod*. Rustici and Leonardo were intimate friends at this time; so much so that Leonardo was rumoured to be the author of the models for the bronze *St. John the Baptist* group, although Vasari dismisses this as unfounded gossip. This period of friendship and collaboration [1507-1509] however would account for the overt affinity to Leonardo's style throughout Rustici's terracotta *Battle Scenes*. We can therefore assume that these, and probably the present *Rivergod* and its associated group, were made after Rustici's association with Leonardo and before his departure for France in 1528.

10 Venus and Cupid

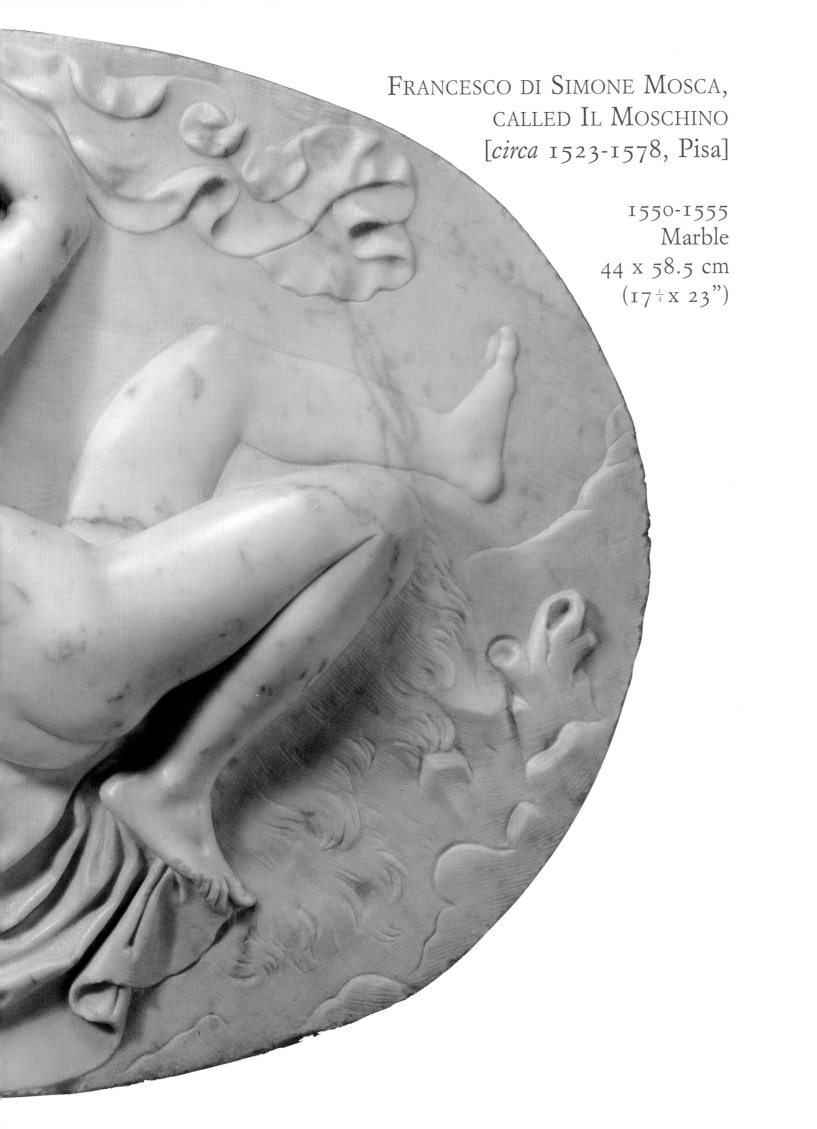

FRANCESCO DI SIMONE MOSCA,
CALLED IL MOSCHINO
[*circa* 1523-1578, Pisa]

1550-1555
Marble
44 x 58.5 cm
(17¼ x 23")

The coupling of Venus and Cupid was a popular theme throughout the Renaissance, and can be seen in varying thematic schemes. While certain compositions find legitimisation through Greek and Roman mythology, like that of "Venus consoling Cupid stung by a bee" or the "Punishment of Cupid", that of an erotic overtone is derived from ancient prototypes and finds no literary lineage. As Cupid was the child god of love, and often mischievous, Venus' significance as his mother is at times overshadowed by her ultimate position as the goddess of love and fertility. Typically paired as more of a symbolic pendant to the other, the present overtly erotic composition of Venus and Cupid *reflects a contemporary aesthetic, fuelled by such works as Bronzino's,* An Allegory with Venus and Cupid, *dated to 1540-1550 and now in the National Gallery, London. (fig. 1)*

By the middle of the 16th century there was a distinct fashion for the erotic in art, instigated in part by the archaeological finds, primarily in Rome, of ancient prototypes of a surprisingly explicit flavour, images of which were disseminated throughout Europe as engraved, painted and sculpted copies.[1] An ancient sarcophagus, now in the Museo Nazionale, Naples, provides a clear example of these original compositions, as its continuous scheme of carved revelry shows a satyress teasing and fondling a Bacchic herm. Lorenzo Ghiberti is recorded to have

[1] BOBER AND RUBINSTEIN, *Renaissance artists and antique sculpture*, London 1987, nos. 3-4, 70, 70b and 94.

Fig.1: Agnolo Bronzino (1503-1572), *An Allegory with Venus and Cupid,* National Gallery, London (photo NG Library)

owned an ancient Roman marble relief of exhausted lovers on a bed, and subsequently popularised through Michelangelo's drawings of its evocative orgiastic composition. Another relief depicting the popular myth of Jupiter disguised as a swan and abducting a vulnerable Leda, is later documented as a gift given by Pope Pius IV, and illustrates the acceptance of such classical eroticism extending as far as the Church.

The elongated female form of the present *Venus* is exaggerated through the use of a curved spine and impossible posture, a method utilised as early as the antique, employed within the above-mentioned marble relief owned by Ghiberti, and characteristic of the Florentine aesthetic of which Il Moschino was an integral part. Led by such early proponents as Francesco Salviati [1510-1563], Agnolo Bronzino [1503-1572] and Jacopo da Pontormo [1494-1556], Florence saw the development of what became later known as High Mannerism; an aesthetic of convoluted composition, agitated posture and mythological subject to which the present relief of *Venus and Cupid* belongs. Correspondences in composition and technique categorise this present relief as an addition to the known works of Il Moschino, and interestingly link a relief of similar subject matter now in the Victoria and Albert Museum to the same artist.²(fig. 2). Admired amongst discerning Florentine collectors, Il Moschino helped to popularise the Mannerist style, exemplified in a marble relief of *Actaeon watching Diana and her Nymphs*

Fig. 2: Francesco di Simone Mosca, *Venus and Cupid*, marble, Victoria and Albert Museum, London (©V&A Picture Library)

Fig.3: Francesco di Simone Mosca, *Venus and Adonis*, Nelson-Atkins Museum, Kansas City.

Bathing presented to Cosimo de Medici and today in the Museo Nazionale del Bargello, Florence.[3] The sinuous body type, problematic postures and distinctive features that characterise the various female figures that fill this *Actaeon and Diana* composition, are the same as that of the present *Venus and Cupid* relief, and include as well Il Moschino's *The Fall of Phaeton* marble now in Berlin and dated to about 1555.

Francesco di Simone Mosca was praised by Vasari for his graceful compositions,[4] a refinement of line easily appreciated in the present *Venus and Child* relief and characteristic of the entire range of his known production. Beginning in his family workshop in Orvieto, Il Moschino initiated his style through such commissions as that for the magnificent *Altar of the Magi* in Orvieto cathedral. Later and following the death of his father, Il Moschino closed the family workshop and began in earnest to build a reputation that would eventually find him favour with Cosimo de Medici. As a direct result Il Moschino won commissions to decorate the Annunciation chapel (1558-63) and that of the *Coronation of the Virgin* in Pisa Cathedral.[5] It is likely that the present relief was the result of a private commission, possibly for installation in a home, and would have occupied a similar place as that, newly recognised, in the Victoria and Albert Museum, London. An amorous group of *Venus and Adonis* (fig. 3) carved by Il Moschino for the Strozzi's courtyard in Banchi, near Rome,[6] is evidence of his prominence amongst the highest echelon of patronage in Italy; and in its emotive character, suggested through posture, exaggerated grace of line, and soft drapery, one sees the same Mannerist vernacular as that observed within the erotic playfulness of the present *Venus and Child*.

[3] *Magnificenza alla corte dei Medici*, exhib. cat., Museo degli Argenti, Palazzo Pitti, Florence, September 1997-January 1998, p. 44, no. 14, illus., entry by Davide Gasparotto.
[4] GIORGIO VASARI, *Le vite de' piú eccelenti scultori ed architettori*, ed. by G. MILANESI, VI, Florence 1881, pp. 305-11.
[5] CIARDI, CASINI AND TONGIORGIO TOMASI, *Scultura a Pisa tra Quattro e Seicento*, Pisa 1987, pp. 189-218.
[6] Today this statue of *Venus and Adonis*, dated to 1553-58, is in the Nelson-Atkins Museum, Kansas City.

RELATED LITERATURE:

CASINI, C., in *Ciardi, Casini and Tomasi, Scultura a Pisa tra Quattro e Seicento*, Pisa, 1987.
GASPAROTTO, D., *Magnificenza alla corte dei Medici. Arte a Firenze alla fine del Cinquecento*, Palazzo Pitti, Florence, 1998.
VASARI, G., *Le Vite de' piú eccellenti pittori scultori ed architettori*, ed. MILANESI, G., IV, Florence, 1881, pp. 305 311.

11 Monkey holding a young monkey

Camillo Mariani
[Vicenza, 1567 - Rome, 1611]

Bronze
53 cm high (21", head to seat)
55.5 cm high (21", head to foot of bent leg)
63 cm. high (24", head to tip of outstretched foot)

Provenance:
Francesco Maria II della Rovere (1549-1631),
Duke of Urbino; commissioned in 1595-96
for garden fountain at Miralfiore, his villa outside Pesaro.
Vittoria della Rovere (1622-94),
Grand Duchess of Tuscany (1637);
still at Miralfiore in 1777.

The mother monkey sits with a young monkey (head and shoulders missing) clasped to her breast and looking over her shoulder: four fingers or toes of another monkey grip the right forearm of the young monkey's left arm which dangles over its mother's back. The composition and the extremely naturalistic treatment of the monkeys' coat and features, portrayed without a hint of sentimentality, suggest that this family group was intended to be seen fully in the round and from close quarters.

[1] J. TURNER (ED.), *The Dictionary of Art, London and New York*, 1996, vol. 27, pp. 274-275, entry by S. Eiche.
[2] BURNS 1979, p. 133.
[3] SCHMIDT 1998, pp. 72 and 77. Respectively 'To the Venetian sculptor for the monkeys of the fountain of Miralfiore' and 'For copper and other things to make the above-mentioned monkeys'.
[4] BURNS 1979, passim; FRUHAN 1986, pp. 353-424; OSTROW 1996, vol. 20, p. 412.
[5] GRONAU 1936, pp. 271-272; BURNS 1979, pp. 7-8; SCHMIDT 1998, p. 72 and note 208 (full archival reference).

The present bronze was unknown until recently and it is an important addition to a set of three other bronze monkeys which have long adorned a fountain in the Boboli Gardens, Florence. The traditional attribution to Giambologna is, however, incorrect. Recent research by Clara Tarca and Eike Schmidt proves that they were commissioned in the mid-1590s by Francesco Maria II della Rovere (1549-1631)[1], Duke of Urbino, for a fountain in the centre of a raised formal garden at Miralfiore, his villa outside Pesaro, and that Camillo Mariani was paid for them in November 1596.

The monkey fountain at Miralfiore is Mariani's most important work in bronze and stands on a par with the statues in marble and stucco which he created for Popes Clement VIII and Paul V after his arrival in Rome in 1597. Mariani raised the art of stucco sculpture to an unprecedented position in Rome, and his dynamic, pictorial and highly expressive style was of fundamental importance to his pupil, Francesco Mochi, and to the second generation of sculptors in the papal capital. He prepared the way for younger artists such as Mochi, Alessandro Algardi and Gianlorenzo Bernini. As Rodger Burns puts it, "Mariani's personal explorations carried him into a world of aesthetic accomplishment unglimpsed by his contemporaries, and his art is a true precursor of the Baroque."

The monkeys for the fountain at Miralfiore were about to be cast when, on 8 November 1596, "the Venetian sculptor" was paid 240 scudi for them (presumably the models in clay or stucco) – *Al scultor[e] ven[ezia]no p[er] le scimie della fonte di Miraf[ior]e* – and another *182 scudi was paid out for copper and other materials to be used in the casting process* – *Per rame et altre cose p[er] far[e] le soprad[ett]e scimie.*[2] Camillo Mariani can be identified as this Venetian sculptor (although, strictly speaking, he came from Vicenza in the Veneto, not from Venice itself).[3] He was recommended to the Duke of Urbino on 13 May 1595 by Vincenzo Scamozzi (1548-1616) and presented one of Scamozzi's drawings to the Duke.[4] A few weeks later, in June 1595, "the new Venetian sculptor" appears for the first time in the ducal account book – *Per il xpo [sic] morto di cera fatto dal nuovo scultore venetiano 20 [scudi].*[5] The proximity of these dates and the fact that Mariani was born,

[6] SCHMIDT 1998, pp. 72 and 77. 'For the dead Christ of wax made by the new Venetian sculptor'.

[7] BURNS 1979, pp. 2-5 and 29-37; FRUHAN 1986, pp. 362-363; SCHMIDT 1998, p. 72.

[8] TARCA 1997, pp. 10-12; SCHMIDT 1998, p. 71 and note 195.

trained and active in the Veneto are compelling reasons to identify him as the sculptor of the monkeys on the fountain at Miralfiore. Mariani had worked in Venice on Scamozzi's Marciana Library (1588-91) and he may also have worked with him in the 1580s on the sculptural decoration of the Teatro Olimpico in Vicenza, their mutual birthplace.[6]

The marble fountain at Miralfiore for which the bronze monkeys were commissioned in the mid-1590s is probably a fountain dating from the previous decade. The gesso model of the *vaso* [vase] for a fountain at Miralfiore had been completed by 8 July 1583; it was designed by Giulio da Thiene in consultation with Giovanni Bandini and made by Piermaria, Bandini's assistant: it had been constructed from late Antique marbles salvaged from Ravenna by 30 December 1584.[7] Giulio da Thiene came from a noble family in Vicenza and was well-known to Scamozzi, as his 1595 letter to the Duke makes clear. The close connections between these three craftsmen from Vicenza further strengthens the case for identifying Mariani as the sculptor of the monkeys on the fountain.

The finished appearance of the monkey fountain at Miralfiore is captured in a view of the villa and gardens painted in tempera by Francesco Mingucci in 1626 (fig. 1).[8] This shows four monkeys sitting on the rim of the quadrilobate basin of

Fig. 1. Francesco Mingucci, *Miralfiore*, 1626, tempera. Biblioteca Apostolica Vaticana, Rome.

the fountain, each perching where the curving walls intersect. They look across the
water basin towards a central element from whose apex spout jets of water. In
Mingucci's painting the details of this central element are obscure and a better clue
to its composition is a much later description given by Antonio Bambozzi and
Domenico Massi in a survey of the grounds dated 27 November 1777 – ...*una
vaschetta centinata di pietra con sua fontana in mezzo, che cade in un piccolo catinetto
di bronzo, cui è sostenuto da quattro scimmiotti parimenti di bronzo...*[9] Whether this
means a single group of four monkeys or four individual monkeys is impossible to
say, but it seems most likely that the monkey presented here formed part of this
central element – especially since the surface of the bronze was covered with lime
deposits (recently removed) and a water mark is still visible around the seated
monkey's hips.

Two facts further support this proposition. One is that four fingertips of a third
monkey grip the young monkey's arm and there are marks where the rest of its
body was attached, indications that the monkey presented here formed part of a
more intricate composition than the freestanding monkeys perched on the rim. The
second is that by 1655 at least three single monkeys – presumably from the rim –
had been transferred to Poggio Imperiale in Florence by Vittoria della Rovere
(1622-94), Grand Duchess of Tuscany as a result of her marriage in 1637 to
Ferdinando II de' Medici: they are described in 1655 at Poggio Imperiale as – *Due
scimmie anzi tre di metallo di getto in vari gesti condotte dalla Ser.[enissi]ma
[Granduchessa Vittoria della Rovere].*[10] Proof that these monkeys came from the

[9] Rome, Biblioteca Apostolica
Vaticana, *Codices Barberiniani
Latini* 4434, c. 12 (Mingucci
1991, facsimile, no. 12); TARCA
1997, note 25 on p. 60, fig. 8;
SCHMIDT 1998, p. 72 and note
206 on p. 99.
[10] Rome, Archivio di Stato,
Camerale III, busta 2445; TAR-
CA 1997, p. 36 and note 70;
SCHMIDT 1998, p. 72 and note
207. 'A curved small, ribbed
[cusped?] basin of stone with its
fountain in the middle, which
falls into a small dish bowl of
bronze, which is held up by
four young little monkeys likewise of bronze'.

Fig. 2b. *Fontana delle Scimmie*, detail, Giardino del Cavaliere, Boboli Gardens, Florence.

[11] Florence, Archivio di Stato, Guardaroba Medicea 657, fol. 15 recto. 'Two monkeys, in fact three, of cast metal in various poses taken by her Serene Highness'. For Vittoria della Rovere, see *The Dictionary of Art*, 1996, vol. 21, p. 28, entry by S. Mascalchi.

[12] *Relazione, e Nota delli stabili, e semoventi pertinenti alla Serenissima principessa Vittoria Feltria della Rovere, nello Stato di Urbino* (Florence, Archivio di Stato, Ducato di Urbino, classe III, filza 17, fasc. 1, fol. 110; cited in TARCA 1997, intro. by FRANCO PANZINI, p. 6 and note 6 on p. 63, and in SCHMIDT 1998, note 207 on p. 99). 'Fountain with statuettes of bronze representing monkeys in various acts'.

fountain at Miralfiore is provided by an inventory drawn up in November 1631, after the death of Vittoria's grandfather (ob. April 1731), in which the monkey fountain is described amongst her movable and immovable possessions as *fontana con statuette di bronzo rappresentanti scimmie in diversi atti*.[11] In short, the three single monkeys now in the Boboli Gardens are likely to have come from the marble rim of the fountain at Miralfiore and the present mother and child group to have formed part of the support of the central bronze fountain.

The three monkeys from the rim of the Miralfiore fountain have occupied a ledge on the base of a fountain in the Boboli Gardens since the 1830s (fig. 2 and fig. 2b). It has long been assumed that they were made for Giambologna's *Samson and the Philistine fountain* of 1566-1570, even though they have little in common with the facture of smaller monkeys which have a better claim to be by Giambologna.[12] Because of this association, the Boboli monkeys from Miralfiore have been attributed wrongly to Giambologna or to Pietro Tacca, his chief assistant.[13] Nonetheless, the history of the three monkeys which Vittoria della Rovere took from Pesaro to Florence is such an integral part of the history of the monkey fountain at Miralfiore that an account of their later history is pertinent in this discussion.

Fig. 3. Niccolò Boldrini, *Caricature of the Laocoön*, woodcut, after Titian. Davison Art Center, Wesleyan University.

A fountain has been recorded in the centre of the garden of the Palazzina del Cavaliere (The Knight's Palace) on a terrace overlooking the Boboli Gardens since the mid-18th century. However, there is no mention of any sculptural adornment until the beginning of the 19th century.[14] It is known that various statues were moved from the Medici villa at Poggio Imperiale circa 1830, e.g. Caccini's *Jupiter and Flora*,[15] and it is probable the three monkeys originally on the rim of the fountain at Miralfiore were also transferred from Poggio Imperiale to the Boboli Gardens at this time. Indeed, the monkeys and the marble putto now atop the Boboli fountain were all recorded in a grotto at Poggio Imperiale in 1655 and 1695 respectively: they have long been together.[16]

Why did Francesco Maria II della Rovere, Duke of Urbino, commission a fountain adorned with monkeys for his raised formal garden at Miralfiore? Given the naturalistic way in which they are conceived and the beautiful setting in which they were placed, it seems most likely that they were intended to reflect the balance between man's creations and the glory of nature, as in the saying *Ars simia Naturae*. Titian, whose own motto was *Natura potentior Ars*, famously caricatured the *Laocoön* group with monkeys as the Trojan priest and his sons (fig. 3),[17] but the intent at Miralfiore is far more respectful. Monkeys were associated with Air (via the sanguine temperament and blood) and with Taste (fruit)[18] – one of the Boboli monkeys holds an apple. Resonances may also have been intended with Water (fountain) and Earth (garden), as well as with Smell (flowers) and Sight (vista and reflections on the water).

[13] *Giambologna* 1978, cat. nos. 182-183 and 199; LEFÉBURE 1984, pp. 184-188; AVERY 1987, p. 268, no. 129; *Von allen Seiten schön* 1995, pp. 380-383, no. 120; see also *Giambologna*, exhib. cat. by C. AVERY, Salander-O'Reilly Galleries, New York, March-April 1998, pp. 136-138.
[14] WILES 1933, p. 64; GURRIERI & CHATFIELD 1972, p. 49; BORSOOK 1979, p. 276; TORRITI 1984, p. 84, no. 18, figs. 64-65.
[15] CAMBIAGI 1757, pp. 38-39; SOLDINI 1789, pp. 24-25; INGHIRAMI 1819, pp. 62-63.
[16] MEDRI 1991, pp. 306-308.
[17] Firenze Florence, Archivio di Stato, Guardaroba Medicea 657, fol. 15 recto (1655); CAPECCHI ET AL 1979, p. 159 (1695).
[18] *Titian and the Venetian woodcut* 1976, no. 40. Our thanks to Rob Lancefield, Davis Art Center, Wesleyan University, Middletown, Connecticut, for providing the photograph (1960.14.5).

[19] J. HALL, *Dictionary of subjects and symbols in art*, rev. ed., London 1979, p. 22 (ape). For monkeys as Vanity, meddlers and bad parents (doting on one child while abandoning another), see A. HENKEL AND A. SCHÖNE (EDS.), *Emblemata. Handbuch zur Sinnbildkunst des XVI. und XVII. Jahrhunderts*, Stuttgart & Weimar 1996, pp. 428-440.

[20] For Bandini's bronze *Boar Hunt*, for which he was paid in November 1583, see SCHMIDT 1998, pp. 75-76, note 240 on pp. 102-103, and pl. 89; R. COPPEL ARÉIZAGA, Museo del Prado. *Catálogo de la escultura de época moderna. Siglos XVI-XVIII*, Madrid 1998, no. 2.

We are extremely grateful to Claudio Pizzorusso for having established the attribution to Mariani and for having undertaken to research the history of the monkeys from Miralfiore on our behalf.

BIBLIOGRAPHY

AVERY, C., *Giambologna. The complete sculpture*, Oxford 1987.

BORSOOK, E., *The Companion Guide to Florence*, London 1979.

BURNS, R. C., *Camillo Mariani: Catalyst of the Sculpture of the Roman Baroque*, Ph. D. dissertation, John Hopkins University, Baltimore 1979 (reproduced by UMI Dissertation Service, Ann Arbor, Michigan).

CAMBIAGI, G., *Descrizione dell'Imperiale Giardino di Boboli*, Florence 1757.

CAPECCHI, G., L. LEPORE AND V. SALADINO, *Collezioni fiorentine di antichità. La Villa del Poggio Imperiale*, Rome 1979.

CELIO, GASPARE, *Memorie delli nomi dell'artifici delle pitture che sono in alcune chiese, facciate e palazzi di Roma*, Naples 1638 (facsimile ed. by E. Zocca,

Mariani had spent his formative years immersed in the artistic traditions of the Veneto, which fused an appreciation of the natural world with the means of expressing its sensual allure through art. With this experience and his expertise as a stucco modeller, Mariani was well-placed to respond to a commission from the Duke of Urbino to create models of monkeys for the fountain in his garden at Miralfiore. Like Giovanni Bandini before him,[19] Mariani made for the ducal court at Pesaro works quite unlike anything he had previously created: almost all their earlier works were large statues in marble or stone. Yet, shortly after his arrival in Pesaro in May/June 1595, Mariani was paid for a wax model of the dead Christ (presumably to be cast in bronze or silver) and payments for the monkeys followed on 8 November 1596. By 25 January 1598 Mariani had arrived in Rome, the only period of his career which has been treated in depth hitherto by art historians. The discovery of the present monkey and recent archival research by Clara Tarca and Eike Schmidt sheds light for the first time on Mariani's sojourn at the Duke of Urbino's court in Pesaro during the mid-1590s. And the Miralfiore monkey presented here joins the three monkeys now in the Boboli Gardens not as works by Giambologna but as bronzes by Camillo Mariani. The brilliance of their conception and execution establishes Mariani as one of the foremost sculptors of animals in 16th century Italy.

Fig. 4a

Milan, 1967).

Giambologna 1529-1608. Sculptor to the Medici, exhib. cat. by C. AVERY AND A. RADCLIFFE, Edinburgh (Royal Scottish Museum) and London (V&A), August-November 1978.

FRUHAN, C. E., *Trends in Roman sculpture circa 1600*, Ph. D. dissertation, University of Michigan, 1986 (reproduced by UMI Dissertation Service, Ann Arbor, Michigan), pp. 353-424.

GRONAU, G., *Documenti artistici urbinati*, Florence 1936.

GURRIERI, F., AND J. CHATFIELD, *Boboli Gardens*, Florence 1972.

INGHIRAMI, F., *Descrizione dell'Imp. e R. Palazzo Pitti di Firenze*, Florence 1819.

LEFÉBURE, A., 'Un singe en bronze de Jean Bologne', *La Revue du Louvre et des Musées de France*, XXXIV, 1984, 3, pp. 184-188.

MEDRI, L., 'Le mutazioni sette-ottocentesche del giardino di Boboli' in *Boboli 90* (acts of Convegno Internazionale di Studi, Florence, 9-11 March 1989), ed. by C. ACIDINI LUCHINAT AND E. GARBERO ZORZI, Florence 1991, 1, pp. 293-310.

MINGUCCI, Francesco, *Città e castella (1626)* ..., facsimile ed. by C. BO, Turin 1991 (Nuova ERI Edizioni Rai, Rome).

Titian and the Venetian woodcut, exhib. cat. by M. MURARO AND D. ROSAND, National Gallery of Art, Washington, Dallas Museum of Fine Arts and Detroit Institute of Art, 1976-1977 (also, as *Tiziano a la silografia veneziana del Cinquecento*, Fondazione Cini, Venice, 1976).

OSTROW, S. F., in *The Dictionary of Art*, ed. J. TURNER, London and New York, 1996, vol. 20, p. 412.

SANGIORGI, F. (ed.), *Diario di Francesco Maria II della Rovere*, Urbino 1989.

SCHMIDT, E. D., 'Giovanni Bandini tra Marche e Toscana', *Nuovi Studi*, 6, 1998, pp. 57-103.

SOLDINI, F. M., *Il Reale Giardino di Boboli nella sua pianta a nelle sue statue*, Florence 1789.

TARCA, C., *Miralfiore. Il parco immaginato. Storia e vedute in cinque secoli*, privately printed by Comune di Pesaro, 1997.

TORRITI, P., *Pietro Tacca da Carrara*, Genoa 1984.

Von allen Seiten schön..., exhib. cat. by V. Krahn et al, Altes Museum, Berlin 1995.

WILES, B. H., *The fountains of Florentine sculptors and their followers from Donatello to Bernini*, Cambridge (Mass.) 1933.

Fig. 4a-c: The monkeys from the Boboli Gardens fountain during restoration at the Palazzo Pitti, 2001.

12 Minerva

Antonio Susini,
[active 1580- died 1624]

cast from a model by
Giambologna [1529-1608]

Bronze
Height: 16 cm (6$\frac{1}{4}$") without base

[1] AVERY AND RADCLIFFE, 1978, catalogue entry 30.
[2] AVERY, C., 1998, illustrated no. 79.

Interestingly this immaculate cast of Minerva, the goddess of war and patroness of the arts, is one of only two prime examples, the other being in the Museo Nazionale, Bargello in Florence. Catalogued by Dr Charles Avery,[1] (fig. 1) for the exhibition Giambologna, Sculptor to the Medici *in 1978, the Bargello example was then thought to be the only cast. Since then a third cast, of lesser quality and more decorative finish, has been identified.[2]*

The dissemination of Giambologna models, both during his lifetime and posthumously, is characteristic of the master's *oeuvre*, distinguishing the present statuette of *Minerva* as an exception. Apart from its immediate quality of casting, the fastidious detail of features, soft drapery folds and warm brown patina encourage an attribution to Giambologna's assistant, Antonio Susini. The distinct rarity of cast, in fact a model that was until recently all but lost, would also argue for a lifetime cast, as it is likely the model was destroyed by the time of Giambologna's death and the Grand Duke Cosimo II's acquisition of the master's workshop, the Borgo Pinti, and its contents.

Contemporary documentary references of 1577-78 cited by Dhanens, refer to the workshop of Giambologna casting certain female figures in silver. Sadly these have not survived, but the specific description of one in particular is easily applicable to the present *Minerva*: 1577 August 12: *Giovanni Bologna riceve come*

Fig. 1, *Minerva,* Museo Nazionale del Bargello, Florence

sopra (una quantità di argento) per gettare due figurine, rappresentanti due donne, una nuda col bastone in mano, e l'altra vestita.[3] And noted on 3 July 1578: *...un'altra figurina staccata dispersa con uno squdo in mano et uno bastone.*[4]

Dhanens remarks of the first reference that a clothed female figure is a rarity for a Giambologna subject. Interestingly, her nude counterpart held a staff (bastone), as did the figurine in the second sited document. While the latter is not specified as clothed, she held the same attributes as the present figure of *Minerva*, a staff and shield.

The rarity, style and quality suggest that this statuette of *Minerva* is an exceptionally important Giambologna model by the technically peerless Antonio Susini.

[3] DESJARDINS, 1883, p.140.
[4] Florence, Archivio di Stato, Guardaroba Reg. 98, fol. 146-7; c.f. CHURCHILL, 1913-14, p.349.

RELATED LITERATURE:

AVERY, C. AND RADCLIFFE, A, ED., *Giambologna 1529-1608, Sculptor to the Medici*, exh.cat, The Arts Council of Great Britain, 1978.
AVERY C., *Museo Civico Amedeo Lia, Sculture: Bronzetti, Placchette, Medaglie*. La Spezia, 1998.
DESJARDINS, A., *La vie et l'oeuvre de Jean Boulogne, d'après les manuscripts inédits recueillis par Foucques de Vagnonville*, Paris, 1883.
DHANENS, E., *Jean Boulogne*, Brussels 1956.

13 APOLLO MUSAGETES

Attributed to
PIERRE DE FRANCQUEVILLE,
also known as FRANCAVILLA
[Cambrai, 1548-1615 Paris]

Bronze
32.5 cm (12¾")

The god of Greek antiquity is holding the lyre, presented to him by Mercury [Ovid, Metamorphoses *2.678-709]; this identifies him as* Apollo Musagetes, *patron of music and poetry and master of the nine Muses dwelling on Mount Parnassus. This representation is clearly inspired by Sansovino's* Apollo *from the Loggetta of the Venice Campanile,[1] itself a reference to the then best-known ancient representation of the god, the marble* Apollo Belvedere *in the papal collection in Rome.*

Only one further version of this bronze is known.[2] And despite its distinguishing character, a compelling attribution has only recently been made to the Flemish sculptor Pierre Francqueville (1548-1615),[3] normally referred to by the Italianised form of his name Pietro Francavilla, on account of his Florentine fame as one of the closest assistants and collaborators of the great Giambologna.

After learning to draw in Paris (c. 1564) and to carve in Innsbruck, probably through working on the tomb to the Emperor Maximilian under Alexander Colijn, Francavilla reached Florence via Rome around 1572 as a qualified sculptor and something of a specialist in anatomical models. With a formal introduction to Giambologna from Archduke Ferdinand of Tyrol, Francavilla went into partnership with the Florentine master, and nurtured a collaboration so seamless, that it is not always feasible to draw a neat dividing line between Giambologna's work and that of Francavilla.

Importantly, the present statuette of *Apollo* represents a crucial expression of both Francavilla's interest in the bronze statuette[4] and of his idiosyncratic

[1] Life size bronze, executed with a *Mercury, Minerva and Pax* in 1540-45.

[2] Art Market, USA: Sotheby's, New York, June 1, 1991, lot 87. A number of inferior variants, cast from this model, one of them in the Metropolitan Museum of Art in New York, have been subjected to various attributions, including the Venetian sculptor, Aspetti.

[3] We are indebted to the expertise of Claudio Pizzorusso for this convincing attribution to Francavilla.

[4] A painted portrait of Francavilla in the Pitti Palace, Florence, shows the sculptor holding a small bronze statuette of fame. (Illustrated plate II, *Francqueville*, 1968.) While another in private hands shows him holding his wax model for the flayed man.

[4] Francavilla, 'Flayed Man', c. 1575, bronze, 25.5 cm. Cracow, Jagiellonian Library. Refer to AVERY, RADCLIFFE, 1978, cat. 192-194; for further Francavilla 'écorché' bronze statuettes and a discussion on their collective stylistic response to the more mannered contemporary aesthetic in anatomical design.

Fig. 1, Francavilla, *Flayed Man*, Jagiellonian Library, Cracow

[5] Illustrated *Francqueville*, 1968, plate XVII.

[6] In 1604 Francavilla went to Paris at the request of Marie de Medici, Queen of France, to model the four slaves for the base of Giambolona's equestrian group to Henry IV on the Pont Neuf. The figure of King and horse were destroyed in 1796, while Francavilla's bronze slaves are in the Louvre, Paris. Illustrated AVERY, 1987, fig. 257.

[7] Palais Ricasoli, Florence, Italy. Illustrated Francqueville, 1968, plate XIII.

treatment of anatomy and casting technique; aspects that effectively set him apart from his master. Sharing explicit stylistic references with known works by Francavilla in marble, as well as bronze, this *Apollo* demonstrates a continuity with his signed bronze statuette of a *Flayed Man*, cast on the same tight, circular plate base, and with corresponding interest in counter balance and arrested motion.[5] (fig. 1)

Here Francavilla has fused certain dependencies on Giambologna, in regards to *Apollo*'s facial features and compositional type, while imbuing them with his own character and style. The slender, all but effeminate, body type of *Apollo*, with jutted hip and bent leg, runs consistently through Francavilla's work, and relates soundly to his marble *David triumphant over Goliath* group in the Louvre.(fig. 2) Moreover, Francavilla's marble statue of Orpheus in the Louvre[6] resonates with the same exaggerated stance, elongated limbs and bent fingers, as the present bronze of *Apollo*. Both are clad in identically fastened sandals that nearly extend beyond the small base on which they stand. A continuity, irrespective of medium, appears to characterise Francavilla's treatment of subject matter and their relationship to the often confining base support, offering ample excuse to extend elongated toes or suggest movement into another space.

Comparisons between the naked body type of the present *Apollo*, and that of other known works in both marble and bronze by Francavilla are numerous; the broad, slender shoulders, distinctive hips and small waist are analogous to Francavilla's handling of the four bronze *Prisoners*, now in the Louvre, and originally cast for the corners of the base to the statue of *Henry IV* formerly on the Pont Neuf.[7] Interestingly Francavilla's bronze statuette of a *Flayed Man* reveals the

Fig. 2, *David Triumphant over Goliath*, Louvre, Paris (Conway Library)

Fig. 3, Francavilla, *Apollo*, Victoria and Albert Museum, London (© V&A Picture Library)

sculptor's attitude to human musculature; a slender, elegant type that is suddenly obvious beneath the bronze 'skin' of the present nude *Apollo*, the marble statue of *Jason* in Florence,[8] or equally, the statue of *Apollo* in the Victoria and Albert Museum, London.[9] (fig. 3)

Sharp facial features characterise Francavilla's work, broadly expressed in marble, as seen in the impressive allegorical statues formerly at Windsor Castle now in the Orangery, Kensington Palace[10]. Emphasised here in small-scale bronze, Apollo's expression is accented by a sharp nose, delineated eyes and pronounced chin, at once reminiscent of Giambologna and evocative of Francavilla's more expressive physiognomy. Francavilla appears to have enjoyed the strength of expression employed through parted lips and slightly opened mouth; a method he employed often as in his figure of *Pomona* at Windsor Castle, the bronze *Prisoners* intended for the Pont Neuf, and his statue of *Orpheus* in the Louvre, the effect of which dramatises the arrested motion of the subject as in the present example of the *Apollo Musagetes*.

[8] Victoria and Albert Museum, London on loan from H.M. the Queen.
[10] For a detailed account of the fascinating history of these statues refer to Scott-Elliot's, 'The Statues by Francavilla in the Royal Collection', *Burlington Magazine*, March 1956.[7]

RELATED LITERATURE:

AVERY, C., *Giambologna, the Complete Sculpture*, London 1987.
AVERY, C., *Francavilla*, in J. TURNER (ed.), The Dictionary of Art, London 1996
AVERY, RADCLIFFE, *Giambologna 1529-1608. Sculptor to the Medici*, Arts Council of Great Britain exhibition, Edinburgh & London 1978.
FRANCQUEVILLE, R., *Pierre de Francqueville, Sculpteur des Médicis et du roi Henri IV*, Paris 1968.
POPE-HENNESSY, J., *Italian High Renaissance and Baroque Sculpture*, London, second edition 1970.
SCOTT-ELLIOT, A. H., 'The Statues by Francavilla in the Royal Collection', *The Burlington Magazine*, March 1956.

14 Nessus and Deianira

Attributed to
BARTHÉLEMY PRIEUR
[Bersieux 1536-1611 Paris]

Bronze
20.5 x 17.5 cm (8 x 7")

The subject is the abduction of Deianira, wife of Hercules, by the centaur Nessus. This particular variation on a well-known composition closely relates to the original model instituted by Giambologna and first mentioned in documents from the archives of the Salviati family in 1575.[1] Camins suggests that Prieur may have known about Giambologna's compositions through his disciple Pietro Francavilla (1548-1615), who was a Frenchman and trained in Paris. Indeed the inventory of Prieur's estate in 1611 lists not only models of his own and after the antique, but over seven hundred drawings predominantly of Italian sculpture.

This fine bronze group of *Nessus and Deianira* corresponds with various other works by Prieur, and while this model is as yet unrecognised in Prieur's *oeuvre* it may well be one of many that remain unidentified during a short period after 1594, the year both of Prieur's appointment to the post of *sculpteur du roi* by Henry IV and of the capitulation of Paris. A characteristic proportion, facture and smooth contours immediately recall acknowledged works by Prieur of this period, in particular a figure group of *The Abduction of a Sabine Woman* exhibited by Daniel Katz Ltd in 1996. (fig. 1)

Encouraged by a significant commission for a sideboard in cedar-wood ornamented with countless modern bronze statuettes, amongst which was the *Henry IV of France on horseback crushing his enemies*,[2] it is clear today that there

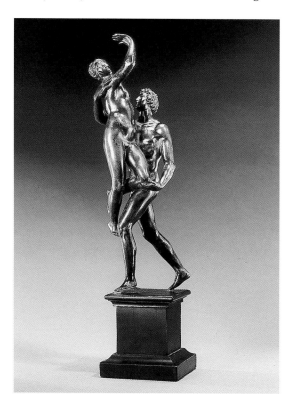

[1] RADCLIFFE AND AVERY 1978/79. Refer to pages 109-116 for the development of the *Nessus and Deianira* subject group.
[2] Victoria and Albert Museum, London.

Fig. 1, Prieur, *Abduction of a Sabine Woman,* Private collection, New York

[3] Private collection, London. Refer to illustration on page 298 in MARTIN, ED, 1992.

[4] At least five casts of this model are known, with examples in the Fitzwilliam Museum, Cambridge, the Metropolitan Museum of Art, New York; The Thyssen-Bornemisza Collection and with Daniel Katz, Ltd, London.

RELATED LITERATURE:

AVERY, C., RADCLIFFE, A., *Giambologna, Sculptor to the Medici*, London 1978-9.
BEAULIEU, M., 'Description raisonnée des sculptures du Musee du Louvre', vol. II, *La Renaissance Française*, Paris, 1978, pp.152-60.
BRIERE, AND LAMY, 'L'Inventaire de Barthélemy Prieur, sculpteur du roi', *Bull. Soc. Hist. Protestantisme Fr.*, xcvi-xcvii, 1949-1950, pp. 41-68.
CAMINS, L., *Renaissance & Baroque Bronzes from the Abbot Guggenheim Collection*, exhibition catalogue, M.H. de Young Memorial Musem, 1988.
MARTIN, I., ED., *Renaissance and Later Sculpture from the Thyssen-Bornemisza Collection*, London 1992.

was a surge of activity on the part of Prieur in the genre of the bronze statuette by the middle or second half of the 1590s. An extant Louvre inventory, compiled on 28 September 1603, supports this claim, and mentions the sideboard including frustratingly vague, though impressively numerous, descriptions of the many statuettes that decorated its surface. Prieur's definitive authorship of the *Henry IV* group, made for this commission, permits little room for doubt that Prieur would have been responsible for the entire bronze commission.

While specifics of the many bronze statuettes mentioned in the Louvre inventory are ambiguous, the document indisputably associates Prieur with a large number of statuettes, encompassing subjects of figures in various postures and animal groups that far extend those so far ascribed to Prieur. Various other groups, including the *Lion attacking a horse*,[3] and the *Lion Walking*,[4] (fig.2) are now acknowledged Prieur models based on their similitude with the *Henry IV* group in the Victoria and Albert and the collective effect of the significant cedar wood sideboard commission.

Accepting that the production type of Prieur and his workshop remains in flux, as more and more material surfaces in the form of stylistic comparison and written document, it would be likely, based on both, that the present *Nessus and Deianira* group belongs to Prieur, and falls within the period after 1594, a time when he was not involved in a single monumental commission, and a period when it is known Prieur actively promoted the advance of the small statuette.

Fig. 2, Prieur, *Lion Walking*, Daniel Katz Ltd, London

15 Head of a Child

Attributed to
HENDRICK DE KEYSER
[Utrecht 1565 – 1621 Amsterdam]

Bronze
7.5 x 6 cm (3 x 2½")

The significance of Hendrick de Keyser, the celebrated city-architect and sculptor of Amsterdam, in the development of the small-scale bronze in Northern Europe has only recently been recognised.[1] Hendrick de Keyser's influence over architectural advances[2] and public monuments, for example that of the tomb to William the Silent, Prince of Orange,[3] is well understood, but a growing number of statuettes is still emerging. Initiated by the recognition of an initialled and dated statuette of Mercury in Amsterdam,[4] and later with the discovery by Avery in 1971 of a bronze group Orpheus and Cerberus, now in the Victoria and Albert Museum,[5] new light was shed on old inventories[6] pertaining to de Keyser's production, de Keyser has now emerged on a par with Willem van Tetrode and the better-known Adriaen de Vries, effectively representing the apogee of what was then a recent tradition of small scale bronze sculpture. After de Keyser's death few bronze statuettes were made in the Netherlands and the initiative passed to Paris and Italy.

This animated head of a young child corresponds with a group of similarly modelled statuettes and bronzes that are now ascribed to Hendrick de Keyser. Together they indicate his fascination with the rendering of human emotion and its effects on the physiognomy. Here we see what appears to be a contented child, lips parted and eyes looking straight forward, as if concentrating on an object or absorbed with a person before him. Characteristics of style such as the deep-set eyes surrounded by expressive folds of skin, slightly protuberant lips, sharp nose and a creased, fleshy neck, as well as the tousled curls of hair, deeply worked and moving outward from the crown to a distinctively high line, exposing a rounded forehead run consistently throughout parallel works known to be by de Keyser.

Two bronze busts, each of *A Crying Child*, emerged in London at different times, one now at the Victoria and Albert Museum,[7] and were recognised by Avery as works of de Keyser on account of their obvious dependence on the child torch bearer that decorates the tomb to *William the Silent*, de Keyser's most important work, and the source by comparison with which various small statuettes by the sculptor have been attributed. The tomb is dotted with bronze statuettes of *Mourning Putti* that sit along its high edge, feet dangling in the air, and in the specific case of the torch bearer, arms held at shoulder height balancing against the weight of the heavy torches he holds in either small hand.[8] Here between furrowed brow and seemingly quivery lip, we see a small child at the moment just before a deluge of tears and outburst of uncontrolled emotion. A small bronze bust in the Palazzo Venezia, Rome, also ascribed to de Keyser, considers the face of a young boy on exactly the same brink of tearful emotion.[9] Both busts of *A Crying Child*

[1] AVERY, 1981.

2 Architectural projects include: gateway ornaments of the Tuchthuis (house of correction, 1598); those on the Spinhuis-poortje (spinning house gateway, 1607); reliefs for the Bergpoot (Berg Gate) in Deventer (dated from 1619, now in Rijksmuseum, Amsterdam); and decorations for the outside of a house in Oudewater (1601); the Oostindisch Huis (East India House, 1606) in Amsterdam which it is believe he built as well as ornamented its impressive façade.

3 The States General commissioned de Keyser in 1614 to design this important funerary monument in Delft, and it remains today as the sculptor's best-known work and also the most important piece of sculpture of this period in Northern Europe.

4 [Height: 32.3 cm] Signed with a monogram 'HDK' and dated '1611'. Rijksmuseum, Amsterdam.

5 [Height: 35.8 cm.] Stated to have come from the collection of Lord Swansea. Purchased by the Victoria and Albert Museum, London (inv.no. A. 5-1972).

6 Refer to AVERY'S article, reprinted in 1981, for explanation of the existence of important inventories relating to de Keyser's small-scale bronze production. He matched descriptions in these papers, with for example the *Mercury* and the *Orpheus* and all the busts of emotive children.

7 See figs. 18 and 19, AVERY, reprinted 1981. A marble bust of this same subject is also ascribed to de Keyser, and is in the Statens Museum for Kunst, Copenhagen. [inv.no.5515]

8 Avery, reprinted 1981. See illustration fig.22.

9 Zuraw, 1996, catalogue entry 12, p. 62.

10 These quasi-scientific studies of human appearances and psychology fascinated Hendrick de Keyser, and may well have been

stimulated by contemporary medical study or theory which was well advanced in Amsterdam (cf. Rembrandt's picture of *The Anatomy Lesson* of Dr. Tulp). Hendrick de Keyser's assiduous interest in human emotion anticipated the "physiognomic" busts of Franz Xavier Messerschmidt, and is attested through the contemporaneous painting of the *Adoration of the Magi* dated 1619 by Hendrick ter Brugghen, that, as noted by Avery, introduces as the Christ Child an uncompromisingly realistic new-born baby, its skin still in loose folds and its face strangely reminiscent of an old man.

[11] Attributed to de Keyser by Avery on the basis of photographs. Height 17 cm. Present whereabouts unknown.

12 Giambologna, *Mercury*. Bronze. Museo Nazionale del Bargello, Florence.

RELATED LITERATURE:

AVERY, C., 'Hendrick de Keyser as a sculptor of small bronzes', reprinted in *Studies in European Sculpture*, AVERY, ed., London 1981, p. 175.

AVERY, LAING, *Finger Prints of the Artists, European Terra-Cotta Sculpture from the Arthur M. Sackler Collections*, Washington, DC and Boston, MA, 1980-1981.

J. LEEUWENBERG AND W. HALSEMA-KUBES: *Beeldhouwwerk in het Rijksmuseum: Catalogus* [Sculpture in the Rijksmuseum: a catalogue], The Hague and Amsterdam, 1973, nos. 223-33.

ZURAW, S., ED., *Masterpieces of Renaissance and Baroque Sculpture from the Palazzo Venezia*, Rome, Georgia Museum of Art, October 5-November 24, Georgia, 1996.

Fig. 1, Giambologna, *Mercury*. Bronze. Museo Nazionale del Bargello, Florence.

study the moments following the accumulated emotion of the torch bearer, where we are presented with an accurate record of physiognomic distortion under the stress of what may be pain, anger or frustration; the child's head thrown back, eyes tightly shut against streams of tears and mouth open in a scream of the type only capable of a young child. Stylistically both examples of *A Crying Child* embrace that of the present *Bust of a Child*, and together we see de Keyser ignoring the idealised Renaissance putto, and replacing this notion with that of a vigorous, quintessentially human baby.[10]

Interestingly, a palm-wood high relief of a *Child in Pain* was sold in Amsterdam in 1897, and while now lost and only known through photographs, is undoubtedly a further work by de Keyser,[11] and part of the emotively charged group in discussion. Bearing obvious stylistic affinities to the present *Bust of a Child*, as well as those already mentioned of this type, the child has a bee on his forehead, identifying the wild scream as that of pain.

The homogeneity of this group of child studies rests not only on their stylistic affinities, but their obvious derivation from those putti that characterise Giambologna's production, and in particular the head of *Zephyr*, which Hendrick de Keyser must have known, that served as the precarious base from which the famous Mercury[12] balanced, as if on the streams of wind blown from the puffed cheeks of the wind-god (fig. 1). If one is to look at the present *Bust of a Child* from its side, creating a comparable silhouette, the associations of full cheeks, sharp nose, forehead and curls with that of Giambologna's head of *Zephyr* is apparent.

16 A Leaping Horse

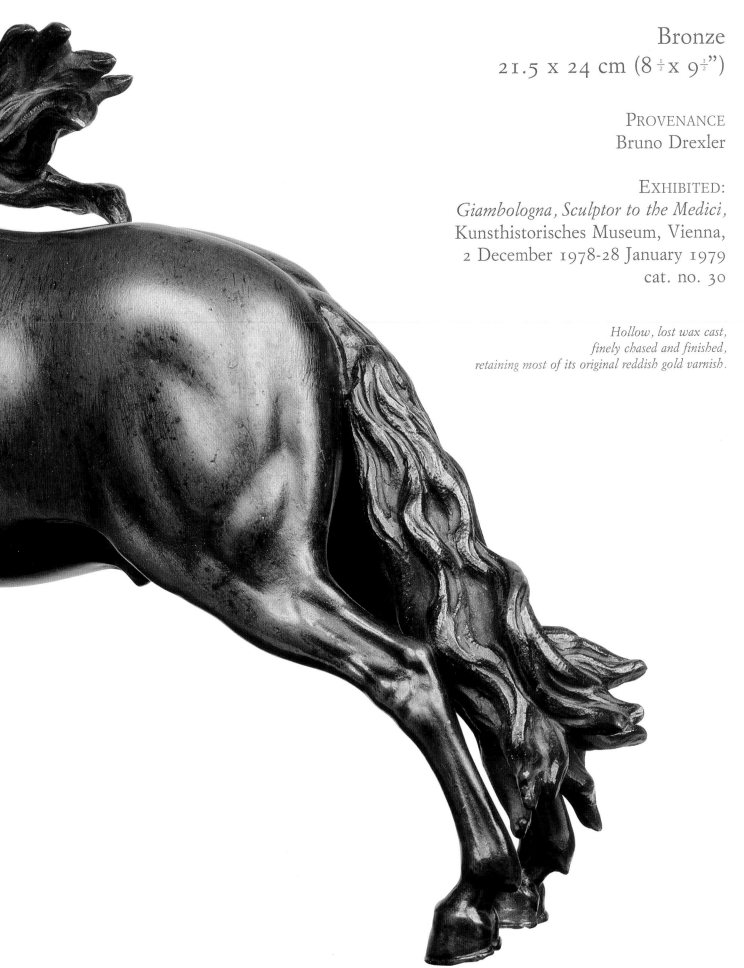

FERDINANDO TACCA
[Florence, 1619-1686]

Bronze
21.5 x 24 cm ($8\frac{1}{2}$ x $9\frac{1}{2}$")

PROVENANCE
Bruno Drexler

EXHIBITED:
Giambologna, Sculptor to the Medici,
Kunsthistorisches Museum, Vienna,
2 December 1978-28 January 1979
cat. no. 30

Hollow, lost wax cast,
finely chased and finished,
retaining most of its original reddish gold varnish.

The horse launches into the air with the vigorous leap of the corvetta *as described in the contemporaneous instruction books, such as Federigo Griso's influential* De equitato *of 1552.*[1] *The dynamism of this movement permits the exposure of Ferdinando's most idiosyncratic aspects of style, encouraging an unrestrained, continuous line and exquisite surface finish. This superior cast plays a crucial role in the delineation of both the stylistic and technical differences between Pietro and his son Ferdinando Tacca.*

This particular model of a *Leaping Horse* is one of a small group of the same subject, all of which have been attributed, at various times, to Giambologna, Pietro Tacca and – most convincingly – Ferdinando Tacca. By 1619 the institution of the walking horse and stately rider was solidified through various equestrian monuments from Giambologna's workshop, found not only in Florence, but also in Paris and Madrid. In response to these models of horses in slow movement Pietro Tacca placed his definitive stamp with a uniquely signed bronze model for a public monument to Carlo Emmanuele of Savoy with a vigorously leaping steed[2]. Through stylistic and technical comparisons with this signed model we can develop a comprehensive means of deciphering equestrian bronzes by Pietro and his son Ferdinando Tacca.[3]

Several versions of the present model exist, and interestingly that in the Museo di Palazzo Venezia, Rome, (fig. 1) and the Bargello in Florence, are paired with a complementary variant of a horse performing the *posata*.[4] (fig.2) Whether the present *Leaping Horse* was conceived as one of a pair is hypothetical, while distinct comparisons between each model and the present example include a typical early to mid 17th century Florentine facture, particularly fine finish and a notable reddish varnish indicating the repertoire of the Grand Ducal workshops.

[1] See JUSTI, *Miscellaneen...* Berlin, 1908, vol.II, p.266 for classical positions of the rearing horse.
[2] See catalogue number 163, p.182 in AVERY AND RADCLIFFE, ED., 1978-9.
[3] A colossal equestrian monument commissioned by King Philip IV of Spain to Pietro Tacca, was unfinished at the time of the sculptor's death in 1640, and was therefore completed by his son Ferdinando. This monument plays a further crucial role in the study of the various and independent styles of the father and son.
[4] Illustrations of the examples in the Museo di Palazzo Venezia in Rome are on page 183 in AVERY, RADCLIFFE, 1978-9. And see note 1 for further explanation on the *posata* position, resembling more of a stationary rearing move than that of the forward motion of the present *corvetta*.

Fig. 1, Ferdinando Tacca, *Horse Leaping*, Museo di Palazzo Venezia, Rome

[5] POLLAK, *Raccolta Alfredo Barsanti*, 1924, no.65.
[6] SANTANGELO, *Museo di Palazzo Venezia, Catalogo delle sculture*, Rome, 1954.
[7] Refer to catalogue entries 164, 165 and 167 in AVERY AND RADCLIFFE, ED., 1978-9.

Fig. 2, Ferdinando Tacca *Horse Rearing*, Museo di Palazzo Venezia, Rome

The present model was originally ascribed to Pietro Tacca, in the catalogue of the Barsanti collection[5]. This was later accepted and reiterated by Santangelo when it reached the Museo di Palazzo Venezia.[6] The distinctive type of the present model, with its long flowing mane and tail, large eyes and flared nostrils, neatly correspond with Pietro Tacca's equestrian bronzes, and this earlier attribution was easily accepted.

It was not until 1978, and the compilation for the *Giambologna, Sculptor to the Medici* catalogue that Watson challenges this earlier attribution and re-ascribes both the present model of the *Leaping Horse*, and that of two variations of a rearing horse to Ferdinando.[7] Wilson effectively compares aspects of Ferdinando's Santo Stefano

relief in Florence to the skilfully sensitive surface filing on this group of horse models, and interprets their collective fluidity and lively handling as idiosyncratic to Ferdinando's technique and style. From this point we see the *oeuvre* of Ferdinando emerging separate from that of his father's and not a dilution of the latter, as was once perceived, but a more exuberant style which is characterised by a softer and more elongated line, and fine surface.

RELATED LITERATURE:

AVERY C., *Museo Civico Amedeo Lia, Sculture: Bronzetti, Placchette, Medaglie*. La Spezia, 1998, no.128
AVERY AND RADCLIFFE, ED., *Giambologna, Sculptor to the Medici*, London, 1978-9.
POLLAK, *Raccolta Alfredo Barsanti*, Florence, 1924.
SANTANGELO, *Museo di Palazzo Venezia, Catalogo delle sculture*, Rome 1954.

FRANÇOIS VAN BOSSUIT
[Brussel 1635-1692 Amsterdam]

Circa third quarter 17th century
Ivory
26 x 12.5 cms (10 x 5")

François Bossuit (or van Bossuit) was born in Brussels and following his early training in Antwerp and Brussels, he left for Italy moving first to Florence then to Rome, where he studied antique art and became associated with the 'Schildersbent', a group of Flemish artists living in Rome. Van Bossuit's Italian period saw an evolution in his work, influenced by some of Italy's most commanding personalities, such as Bernini and his fellow Fleming François Duquesnoy. By the year 1685 Van Bossuit returned to the Netherlands, and settled in Amsterdam. Works by Van Bossuit are quite rare, a portion of which may easily be identified from a series of engravings that prove to be accurate document.

The present ivory relief depicting the *Ecstasy of Mary Magdalene* corresponds to a group of carvings ascribed to the hand of the Netherlandish sculptor, François van Bossuit. Van Bossuit's tendency to leave his works unsigned is problematic, but is alleviated by the existence of a catalogue of engravings, designed on the basis of the carver's compositions recorded at the time of Mathys Pool's publication in 1727.[1] Initially meant as an archival document, this compilation now remains as an undisputed reference, effectively securing the authorship of a core group of Van Bossuit's known production. Based on these comprehensive etchings, a group of ivory carvings have come to light that correspond in both documented composition and style. It is through indisputable stylistic and technical relation to this core group of Van Bossuit's documented carvings, that we include the present *Ecstasy of Mary Magdalene* to his production.

Beyond definitive documentation by Barent Graat's etchings, attribution to Van Bossuit must be based on a stylistic continuity with this group, or distinct relationship to the two known signed works by Van Bossuit; *Mercury, Argus and Io*

[1] *Cabinet de L'Art de Schulpture par le fameux sculptureur Francis van Bossuit...*, POOL, M., Amsterdam, 1727.

Fig. 1, Van Bossuit, *The Toilet of Bathsheba*, Wallace Collection, London

[2] Rijksmuseum, Amsterdam [Inv. N.M. 2931]

[3] Wallace Collection, London. [Inv. S263]

RELATED LITERATURE:

Cabinet de L'Art de Schulpture par le fameux sculptureur Francis van Bossuit execute en yvoire ou ébauché en terre, gravées d'aprés les dessins de Barent Graat par Mathys Pool, Amsterdam, 1727.
DEVIGNE, M., 'François Bossuit and Ignaz Elfhafen', *Burlington Magazine*, xlvii, 1925, pp. 40-46.
LEEUWENBERG AND HALSEMA-KUBES, *Beeldhouwkunst in het Rijksmuseum*, Rijksmuseum, Amsterdam, 1973.
PHILIPPOVICH, E., *Elfenbein*, Munich, 1982.
THEUERKAUFF, VON C., *Zu Francis von Bossuit (1635-1692); Beeldsnyder in Yvoor*, Köln, 1975.

in a private collection in Germany, and *Marsyas*. That of *Mercury, Argus and Io* provides a strong parallel in its overall compositional type to the present relief of the *Ecstasy of Mary Magdalene*, where emotive effect, drapery treatment and dramatised posture present further parallels.

A sensuality characterises the present ecstatic posture of Mary Magdalene, and can be compared to many designs preserved by Graat; for example that of *Venus and Adonis*, a portrait of *Lucretia* and *The Death of Adonis*[2] in the Rijksmuseum, Amsterdam. Beyond the natural emotive parallels between that of *The Death of Adonis* and the present *Ecstasy of Mary Magdalene*, striking compositional comparisons can be observed in the position and character of the dying Adonis and the ecstatic Mary Magdalene. Physiognomy, drapery type, and the distinctive winged putti amongst swirling clouds are characteristic to both ivory carvings, and can be plainly observed in a great many reliefs ascribed to Van Bossuit.

The Wallace Collection, London holds a rectangular ivory panel of *The Toilet of Bathsheba*,[3] (fig. 1) and as its design is clearly documented within Graat's etchings, it provides a reliable means of comparative material for the present attribution to Van Bossuit. Distinct parallels in the treatment of the high relief foreground emerging against a sensitively handled low relief distant ground can be seen between the present relief and that of *Bathsheba*. A further comparative relief of the *Annunciation* is in a private collection, London (fig.2) and bears similar relations as that in the Wallace Collection to the present *Ecstasy of Mary Magdalene*.

Far too many comparisons to be mentioned here relate the present relief of the *Ecstasy of Mary Magdalene* to those documented by Graat's engravings, although two in the collection of the Brunswick Museum bear specific mention; that of *Apollo and Daphne* and *Mercury and Psyche*, each carved with parallel sympathy and notably analogous treatment of surface relief. It is known that Graat did not record all of the ivory carvings produced by Van Bossuit, and on the basis of the definitive comparative material that does remain, the present relief can be included as a fine, rediscovered ivory by the accomplished François Von Bossuit.

Fig. 2, Van Bossuit, *Annunciation*, Private Collection, London

18 LEDA AND DANAË

Attributed to
PIERRE LEGROS (THE YOUNGER)
[Paris, 1666-1719, Rome]

Last quarter 17th century
Bronze statuettes
26 and 28.5 cm (10¼ and 11¼") respectively

[1] However, Homer's version of the myth, recorded in both the *Odyssey* [XI, 299] and the *Iliad* [III, 426] is the same as that of Euripides's *Helena* [254, 1497 and 1680] and together differs from the above, instead recording that Tyndareus had lain with Leda in the same night as Zeus, and that only Helen was an offspring of the latter, whereas the other siblings were the children of the king, Tyndareus.

[2] For biographical accounts of Pierre Legros the younger, see J. TURNER (ED.), *The Dictionary of Art*, London and New York, 1996, vol. 19, pp. 88-89, entry by F. DE LA MOUREYRE; SOUCHAL G-L, *op. cit.*, p. 273; *ibid.*, *Supplementary volume, A-Z*, London 1993, p. 145; R. ENGASS, *Early eighteenth-century sculpture in Rome ...*, 2 vols., University Park and London, 1976, pp. 124-131.

[3] J. TURNER (ED.), *The Dictionary of Art*, London and New York, 1996, vol. 18, p. 660, entry by J. S. HALLAM.

[4] "Trois esquisses en terre cuite de LE GROS, représentant, l'une Arianne et Bacchus, l'autre Danaë, recevant la pluie d'or, & le troisième une Léda. Ces esquisses sont faites avec tout le feu, & l'esprit possible, & n'ont jamais été exécutées en marbre" in the *Petit Cabinet sur la Cour* (*Catalogue historique du cabinet de peinture et sculpture française de M. La Live de Jully*, Paris, 1764, pp. 45-46): a virtually identical description is given in M. HÉBERT, *Dictionnaire pittoresque et historique, ou decription d'architecture, peinture, sculpture, gravure...*, Paris 1766, vol. I, p. 123. See also F. SOUCHAL ET AL, *French sculptors of the 17th and 18th centuries. The reign of Louis XIV. G-L*, Oxford 1981, p. 299, nos. 48-50. We are extremely grateful to Françoise de la Moureyre for confirming the accuracy of these references and for transcribing the descriptions.

[5] "Trois figures peu terminées,

The first bronze depicts the moment when the charms of Zeus, disguised as a swan, win over Leda's modesty, while Eros, the spirit of physical love, looks on as a mischievous putto instigating the imminent seduction. Various accounts exist of this mythological subject, the more typical relating that Zeus saw Leda, the wife of Tyndareus, king of Sparta, bathing in the river Eurotas, and immediately fell desperately in love with her. He approached her in the guise of a swan and managed to seduce her, the result of this union being the birth of two sets of twins; Helen and Clytemnestra, and Castor and Polydeuces. Consequently, Leda was accepted amongst the Olympian gods as Nemesis.[1]

The second bronze shows Danaë receiving Zeus in the form of a shower of golden coins, while the putto *at her feet plays the same role of instigator as that in the other group. The eagle, a common representation of Zeus, is shown to indicate his presence. According to Ovid's* Metamorphoses *[4.611], Danaë's father, the king of Argos, was told by an oracle that Danaë's first-born son would kill him. To ward off suitors and his own demise, the king had his daughter locked away in a tower. Zeus, however, penetrated this fortress in the shape of golden coins, driven by his passionate love for Danaë, and the eventual effect of their union was a son, Perseus, who, as prophesied, killed his grandfather accidentally with a discus.*

Both Leda and Danaë were wooed by Zeus, and for this reason it is not surprising that they have been paired, although the existence of such a grouping in sculpture is virtually unknown. Pierre Legros is the only sculptor documented to have created statuettes of *Danaë* and *Leda* during Louis XIV's reign, a period of time Legros spent almost entirely in Rome.[2] Terracotta *bozzetti* of both compositions, as well as of *Bacchus and Ariadne*, belonged to Ange-Laurent de la Live de Jully (1725-1779), the great French collector and patron.[3] They were described in the 1764 catalogue of the latter's collection as 'three sketches in terracotta by Le Gros representing *Bacchus and Ariadne*, *Danaë receiving the golden rain* and *Leda*. These sketches are done with all possible fire and spirit, and have never been executed in marble'.[4] They reappeared in the 1770 sale catalogue of de la Live's collection with cursory descriptions as 'three figures little finished, each 23 cm. high'.[5]

Legros is not usually associated with bronze statuettes and the only documented instance is a pair of *putti* that flank one of the eight candelabra that decorate the altar rail of the chapel of St. Ignatius at the Gesú.[6] Engass's study of payments and other documents establishes the authorship of these and of the seven other pairs of *putti*, finally resolving the problematic issue of their genesis.[7]

Other bronze figures attributed to Legros in 18th century sources are *Flora with Cupid* and *The Satyr Marsyas tied to a Tree*.[8] Although both are larger, measuring 78 cm and 68 cm high respectively, they have stylistic affinities with the present pair of statuettes: for example, Leda's dramatically raised arm and bent neck resembles that of Flora in *Flora with Cupid*. Interestingly, Souchal[9] traces a marble version of the bronze *Marsyas*, also listed as by Legros, to the same Parisian collector, Ange-Laurent de la Live de Jully, and eventually as part of the subsequent sale of the collection in Paris, 2 May 1770, as number 151.

Legros produced various small-scale works for private collectors as well as the large marble statues for which he is better known. The posthumous inventory of Legros' studio contents, dated 14 December 1719, does little to clarify individual compositions, but is proof that Legros was responsible for many more sketches, designs and models than are ascribed to him today. Some of these models were certainly cast in bronze and silver for private individuals, and it is possible that *Leda* and *Danaë* were amongst the fifteen terracotta models by Legros listed in the inventory of his studio contents.[10]

de chacune 8 pouces 6 lignes" (*Catalogue raisonné des tableaux, ... & d'autres objets qui composent le Cabinet de M. de La Live de Jully*, P. Remy, Paris, 2 May 1770 and following days, p. 72, lot 170, under the heading Terre Cuite: the catalogue was printed in 1769 for a sale originally scheduled for 5 March 1770). 1 pouce = 12 lignes = 27.09 mm..
[6] In 1695 Andrea Pozzo prepared the overall design for the chapel, effectively serving as a guide, not rigid, for the large group of artists commissioned for the project. Conveniently, Legros' role is fully documented in an extant contract for his *tableau vivant*. When completed, this grand altar was regarded as one of the most successful of its type, and its reputation remained unparalleled throughout the better part of the following century.
[7] *Ibid.*, p.133
[8] SOUCHAL ET AL, 1981, pp. 298-299, nos. 41 and 42c.
[9] *Ibid.*, p.298.
[10] ENGGASS, 1976, p.130.

RELATED LITERATURE:

BISSELL, G., *Pierre Le Gros, 1666-1719*, Reading, England, 1997.
ENGASS, R., *Early eighteenth-century sculpture in Rome, an illustrated* catalogue raisonné, 2 vols., University Park and London, 1976, pp. 124-131.
SOUCHAL, F. ET AL, *French sculptors of the 17th and 18th centuries. The reign of Louis XIV. G-L*, Oxford 1981, p. 273; *ibid., Supplementary volume, A-Z*, London 1993, p. 145.
TURNER, J. (ED.), *The Dictionary of Art*, London and New York, 1996, vol. 19, pp. 88-89, entry by F. DE LA MOUREYRE.

19 CROUCHING VENUS

Cast from a model by
ANTOINE COYSEVOX
[Lyon 1640-1720 Paris]

Circa 1686-1692
Bronze
66 x 44.5 x 33.6 cms
(26 x 17½ x 13¼")

[1] Translated from the French original. Refer RIPA, C., *Iconologia*, English, translated Motte, B., London, 1709.

[2] SOUCHAL, A-F, p.191. (height: 183 cm) Cosyevox's official capacity secured him a prominent spot in both the decoration of the chateau's interior and throughout the extensive gardens of Versailles. He concentrated on a large group of marble statues, all based on the antique and including the present model of the *Crouching Venus*, each imbued with a certain degree of adaptation that soon characterised Cosyevox's style, and for which there was a distinct and growing fashion. Further works by Cosyevox in this vein and for the Royal gardens include: *Nymph with a Shell* (now in the Louvre), the *Medici Venus* (now untraced) and *Caster and Pollux* (Allee Royale, Versailles).

[3] Sometimes referred to as the 'Synthian Slave', the crouching posture of this similarly draped naked figure complements that of the present *Crouching Venus*, making a visually logical pairing. Refer to PINCAS, 1996, p.76-77 for good colour photographs of both casts as they appear *in situ* today.

[4] SOUCHAL, A-F, p.191-192. Illustrated.

[5] One of these Keller casts, that of the *Laocöon*, was later acquired in Paris by the elder son of Sir Robert Walpole and taken to Houghton Hall in Norfolk where it still remains.

The present Crouching Venus *shows variations on the antique prototype, first recorded in the Villa Medici in Rome, and exists as a fine response to the French interpretation of the Italian antique; a 17th century fashion pioneered by an elite group of sculptors, of which Antoine Coysevox was an integral part. The original marble, now in the Uffizi, Florence, encompasses what is a persistently esoteric rendition of the familiar Venus, believed to represent the goddess immediately after her birth and about to be carried to land on a seashell. Immediately, we see Coysevox's substitution of a tortoise for the original seashell; effectively transforming that of the* Crouching Venus *into an allegorical allusion to 'Modesty', a reference taken from Cesare Ripa's* Iconologia, *and specifically alluding to the passage: "Chaste women should move from their house no more than this animal moves from beneath the roof where nature had confined it."*[1]

Of the many known copies and variations on this antique model of a *Crouching Venus*, the most famous is undoubtedly the marble by Coysevox, completed in 1686 for the garden at Versailles and signed with his own name and that of Phidias, written in Greek.[2] As a departure in its iconographic references, Coysevox's free interpretation of the antique prototype met with overwhelming praise, effectively more than that garnered by the original. In response, the Keller foundry were commissioned to produce a bronze cast of the marble, where it was initially intended for the Chateau at Marly, and since 1871 remains in the gardens of Versailles, placed at the top of an outdoor stairway located at the southern end of the Parterre du Nord, and paired with a cast of *Arrotino*.[3]

Regarded as the most esteemed bronze foundry in France during the 17th century, the Keller brothers, Johan Jacob (1635-1700) and Balthasar (1638-1702), were appointed by the court of Louis XIV, and in 1684 commissioned to carry out a series of large-scale casts from those sculptures that adorned the gardens at Versailles, including that of the present *Crouching Venus*.[4] Coysevox was responsible for a large portion of the sculptural decoration throughout the gardens of Versailles, many of which were eventually cast in bronze by the Keller brothers. While some remain *in situ*, others have dispersed,[5] and documents prove that others were not cast at all on account of the short-lived practice of bronze casting of this scale. Both economic and political responsibility curbed the continuation of this monumental bronze casting project, but not without effectively sparking a fashion for after-antique bronze casts, a demand quickly satisfied by the Keller foundry with smaller, more reasonable casts. A characteristic surface finish, patina

RELATED LITERATURE:

HASKELL AND PENNY, *Taste and the Antique*, London, 1981.
KELLER-DORAIN, G., *Antoine Coysevox: Catalogue raissonne de son oeuvre*, 2 vols, Paris, 1920.
PINCAS, S, *Versailles, The History of the Gardens and their Sculpture*, London, 1996.
RIPA, C., *Iconologia*, English, translated by B. Motte, London, 1709.
SOUCHAL, F., *French Sculptors of the 17th and 18th centuries; The reign of Louis XIV*, vol. A-F, London, 1993.

and casting technique, evidenced by core remains and early bolts within the inside rough walls of this hollow cast, support an early date; probably one produced by the Keller brothers in the last years of the 17th century in response to increased market demands.

20 Portrait of a Gentleman
possibly Joseph Addison (1672-1719)

David Le Marchand
[Dieppe, 1674-1726 London]

Ivory bust
Circa 1704-1710
23.5 x 16.25 cm (10 x 6½")

Provenance:
Mrs Ruth Costantino,
The Connoisseur Inc., New York
(purchased from an unknown source
in London before 1976)
Her private collection
Thence by family descent

Exhibited:
David le Marchand (1674-1726),
An Ingenious Man for Carving in Ivory,
National Gallery of Scotland, Edinburgh;
The British Museum, London;
Leeds City Art Gallery (The Henry Moore Centre),
Leeds, 1996-97, No 79.

[1] Perhaps prompted by the death of his predecessor, Jean Cavalier, who previously served as the Royal ivory portrait carver.

[2] Among the patrons who flocked to Le Marchand upon his arrival to London were Royalty- Queen Anne and King George I; and nobility- The Duke of Marlborough and his daughter Anne, Countess of Sunderland, as well as the Earl of Peterborough and the Privy Councillor, Thomas Brodrick PC; and literati – Guy, Locke, Newton and Wren among many others.

[3] Illustrated as catalogue number 31 in AVERY, 1996. Now in the Victoria and Albert Museum, London.

[4] Furthermore, it has been suggested by Charles Avery, the authority on the life and works of David Le Marchand, that a further explanation for the absence of signature is that it may have originally been one of a pair, probably Addison's wife, and would have faced the present bust with a similarly strongly turned head and gaze, and would have been likely to have held the signature.

[5] KNELLER, *Portrait of Joseph Addison (1672-1719), poet and essayist*. National Portrait Gallery, inv. NPG 3193.

The consequence of David le Marchand on the development of what became, by the later 18th century, definitive English portrait sculpture has until recently gone unrecognised. This itinerant Huguenot ivory-carver, originally from Dieppe, was highly sought from as early as the year 1700, following his move from Edinburgh[1] to London and his immediate introduction to Royal patronage and the prestigious circle of literati and city businessman referred to as the 'British Worthies'.[2] Working ad vivum *– from life – as well as posthumously, Le Marchand's portraits in ivory possessed a revolutionary sense of volume and a characterisation previously unseen in sculpture. Hurdling the constraints of accepted portraiture of the day, David purposely showed his subjects in a variety of angles, carving with similar deliberation on all sides, and effectively immortalising his sitter in a manner that served as inspiration for such sculptors as Rysbrack, Roubiliac and the Scheemakers carving in large scale marble and stone almost a generation later.*

The immediacy and presence that characterises the present portrait bust, possibly of Joseph Addison, separates it from the majority of ivory carving of the early 18th century, and its luxuriant curls, voluminous drapery and exquisite detailing as seen in the wrinkles of an unbuttoned chemise or sliver of a button hole secures it as a definitive work by the eminent David Le Marchand.

Curiously unsigned, a rectangular inserted piece of wood into the back of its ivory base might suggest where at some point the artist's initials, D.L.M, were removed, as Le Marchant often carved his initials on this point of similarly styled busts. Otherwise, it is not unlikely that David signed this work on its original base, now lost, as various other examples remain this way; including a similar sized bust of King George,[3] and two others of Sir Isaac Newton, one now in the collection of the British Museum.[4]

David Le Marchand's relationship with Godfrey Kneller, the principle painter to the King of Great Britain, was significant and has helped in the identification of various unknown sitters common to Le Marchand's extant works. The present identification to the essayist and poet Joseph Addison remains only speculative, based on documented evidence regarding the sculptor's circle of patronage extending into that of the higher echelons of British contemporary literati, as well its likeness to a portrait of Addison painted by Kneller now in the national Portrait Gallery.[5] The similitude of the early 18th century periwig and dress complicates matters, as does the specific casualness of the present sitter's open chemise, effectively pointing to a man at the height of his career, not a

Fig. 1, Le Marchand, *Francis Sambrooke* (b 1662), Collection of Lord Thompson of Fleet, Toronto.

distinguishing means of elimination as all of Le Marchand's sitters were of the same revered status.

The present bust of Addison encapsulates all that is Le Marchand's idiosyncratic style of ivory carving, and can be closely compared to a bust of *Francis Sambrooke*, signed and dated to the year 1704 and possessing the same forcefulness of head turn and gaze.[6] (fig. 1) Adopting a method of utilising wax models by around the time of his move to London, David's busts simultaneously reveal an increased softness to their surface where the ivory appears to lend itself to the curve of a brow or ringlet of hair as easily as the malleability of soft wax. The manner in which Le Marchand drilled the ends of each curl accents their depth and the pliable way in which the drapery encircles the truncated body while complimenting the turn of the sitters head and neck, encourages the viewer's complete attention, and effectively places the present work outside the confines of 'decorative art' and instead within the exalted world of portrait sculpture, years before it had even been defined in England.

[6] Collection of Lord Thomson of Fleet, Toronto. Refer AVERY 1996, catalogue number 58 and colour plate 2.

RELATED LITERATURE:

AVERY, C., 'David Le Marchand, Precursor of eighteenth-century English portrait sculpture', *The British Art Journal*, vol. 1, No.1, 1999, p.27-34.
AVERY, C., *David Le Marchand (1674-726), An Ingenious Man for Carving in Ivory*, London 1996.

21 THE PIED PIPER OF HAMELIN

SIMON TROGER
[Austria, 1683-1768]

Circa 1740
Boxwood, ivory and glass
35 x 26 cms (13¼ x 10¾")

A man in a tattered, cinched garment leans casually against the gnarled trunk of a dead tree, a bundle strapped to his back and a flute in his hand. He gestures theatrically with his left arm and stares thoughtfully to the ground strewn with stones, and a small mouse scurries for cover beneath the exposed roots of the trunk. A leather pouch, heavy with contents hangs across his chest and to one side. His broad brimmed hat is turned up at the sides and ears of wheat are stuck in the band.

The *oeuvre* of Simon Troger is characterised by a remarkable technical virtuosity. Integrating various media within theatrical compositions and figure groups, Troger's later works are quintessentially Baroque and reflect influences from the works of Andreas Faistenberger [1647-1736] in whose workshop Troger worked in Munich prior to setting up his own in Haidhausen.

The exact chronology of Troger's work has not been fully established, for it is impeded by a lack of earlier material, and a curious stylistic disparity between what is believed to be his earlier works[1] and those expected to have been made following his move to Munich. The present figure, *The Pied Piper*, corresponds with works that typify Troger's production after 1733. They are described in an inventory of that year of the Dresden Kunstkammer as 'a series of genre figures' each with measurements exactly, or nearly the same as *The Pied Piper*.[2] Two of the works recorded in the Dresden inventory[3] survive in private collections; *A Charlatan* and a *Street Vendor of Mussels*, and each possess the same degree of dramatised posture

[1] Troger's earliest work is believed to be a large group in wood and ivory of *St Michael Vanquishing Satan*, in the Pitti Palace, Florence, and would have been made during his brief sojourn in Italy from about 1723-25.
[2] See THEUERKAUFF, 1986, pp.267-73.

Fig. 1: Troger, *Chariot with Sylenus*, Hermitage, Moscow. Bridgeman Library, London

[3] See THIEME-BECKER for biographical details on Simon Troger's career.

[4] Victoria and Albert Museum, London, inv. no 1009 to 6-1873. Another impressive religious narrative group of *The Martyrdom of St. Lawrence* is in the Bayerisches Nationalmuseum, Munich, and illustrated in PHILIPPOVICH, p.306. The Bayerisches Nationalmuseum has the most extensive and comprehensive collection of Simon Troger's work.

RELATED LITERATURE:

THEUERKAUFF, C, 'Die Bildwerke in Elfenbein des 16.-19. Jahrhunderts'. *Die Bildwerke der Skulpturengalerie Berlin*, Berlin 1986.
THIEME, U. AND F. BECKER, EDS, *Allgemeines Lexikon der bildenden Künstler von der Antike bis zur Gegenwart*, Leipzig, vol. 33, p. 420.
PHILIPPOVICH, VON, *Elfenbein: Ein Handbuch für Sammler und Liebhaber*, Munich, 1982.

and skill of carving evidenced in the handling of belted drapery, ringlets of hair and naturalistic features.

This *Pied Piper* is congruous with the many figures Troger is known to have produced for one of his favoured patrons, Maximilian III Joseph, Elector of Bavaria, and from this stage, the early 1730s, Troger was utilising similar combinations of materials as that seen in the *Pied Piper*.

The agility with which he handled differing media had an almost illusionistic effect, as if the bits of limewood, ivory, glass and even metal in some cases, are fused together to suggest polished ivory 'skin' peeking through limewood 'tears' in heavy layers of clothes. This same degree of skilful amalgamation can be seen in Troger's large-scale narrative groups; for example *The Judgement of Solomon* in the Victoria and Albert Museum[4] or the remarkable *Chariot with Silenus* in the Hermitage, St. Petersburg, (fig. 1) which display Troger's total manoeuvrability and aptitude with the materials he worked. This fascinating realism is the hallmark of Simon Troger's genius.

22 Baigneuse Assise [Seated Bather]

Attributed to
Etienne-Maurice Falconet
[Paris 1716-1791]

Marble
Circa 1757-1765
72 x 45 cm (28¼ x 17¾")

The Baigneuse Assise *or* Seated Bather *continues a well-known series of representations of women and poses in the attitude of the* Classical Thorn Puller*, enacting a variety of biblical, mythological, and genre scenes that can explain an after-the-bath episode. Initiated by the resounding popularity of his* Nymph descending into the bath *at the 1757 Salon, Falconet responded with an associated group of naked, young women imbued with a subtle dose of vulnerability and eroticism, each in varying stages of bathing. Distinctively women of young, almost indecipherable age and evocative of adolescence, Falconet's series of women introduce* la femme-enfant *for the first time to French sculpture, and effectively respond to the century's* dramatis personae *with Prévost's* Manon Lescaut *and Greuze's* Cruche cassée.

¹ REAU, 1922, plate XXI. The Elms, as well as other Newport mansions, is managed by The Preservation Society of Newport County. Berwind, a wealthy coal baron, died in 1922, and his collection, comprised mainly of French 18ᵗʰ century works of art and paintings, has been largely preserved at The Elms, although certain works are known to be in the Metropolitan Museum, and otherwise disseminated.

Four examples of this *Seated Bather* are documented, each mentioned as part of a group attributed to Falconet in Reau's 1922 monograph of the sculptor, and one illustrated as part of the Edward Julius Berwind Collection, New York, now housed in the family's country residence, The Elms in Newport, Rhode Island¹. Other cited examples of this model, executed in marble and of similar size to the present include; that in the Musée de Lons-le-Saulnier, the private collection of Dr. Werner Weisbach in Berlin and the collection of Baron Edmond de Rothschild, Paris. Over time, and a lack of documented material, it is nearly impossible to track the whereabouts of those beyond that at The Elms, and it is likely that the present *Seated Bather* is one of the two listed in private collections in 1922.

Despite the wide range of bathing figures and bathing subject compositions long-associated with Falconet's production, only that of the *Nymph descending into the*

Fig. 1: Etienne-Maurice Falconet, *Nymph descending into the bath,* 1757, Paris, Louvre

bath (*Nymphe qui descend au bain*) is definitively attributed and dated to the year 1757 on account of its inclusion in the Salon of that year. (fig. 1) Slightly larger in height than that of the present *Seated Bather* (*Baigneuse Assise*), it is carved with parallel sympathy; the water suggested by a highly polished surface in contrast to the rough character of the tree trunk she leans against or the rocky outcrop that she sits. Gradations of surface treatment exemplify the crystalline nature of the clean block of marble used for both the *Nymph descending into the Bath* and the present *Seated Bather*, and is typical of works believed to be part of Falconet's production, where a precision of carving emphasises a 'frosty', almost ethereal quality.

The subsequent public reaction in 1757 to Falconet's *Nymph descending into the bath* was nearly unprecedented and effectively created a fashion for works of this genre, a market demand to which sculptors following in Falconet's wake naturally filled. Sculptors including Jean Antoine Tassaert,[2] the brothers Joseph and Ignace Broche[3] and Gabriel-Christophe Allegrain[4] produced works directly inspired by the success of Falconet's nude bather, and while these responses were typically small-scale statuettes, intended for display on table tops and mantle clocks, they were often left unsigned, leaving a gaping hole for art historical debate and subsequent misattribution. As reasonably suggested by Levitine,[5] the anonymity of such works may well have been deliberate, a result of the imitators of Falconet wishing to disguise their personal responsibility for works in his style, and thereby perhaps enhancing the commercial value of their efforts.

It has been noted as early as 1908 and the publication of the first monograph on Falconet,[6] that caution is needed when referring to nearly all works believed to be by the artist. Unfortunately for us today, Falconet did not always sign his works, and even that of the *Nymph descending into the bath*, now in the Louvre, regarded as of one of his most celebrated works and responsible for initiating an entire subsequent aesthetic, is not signed. A further model of this Salon *Nymph* is today in the Victoria and Albert Museum, London,[7] and it too, is not signed and catalogued with a degree of trepidation that has become synonymous with the works of Falconet. When compared with the almost saturated production of small scale statuettes, both in marble and at Sèvres, initiated by Falconet's *Nymph descending into the bath*, only a small group of larger scale works, like the above mentioned Victoria and Albert Museum example or the present *Seated Nymph*, exist; lashed together by their intermittent text book references to Falconet and an underlining quality of carving that transcends those of the many imitators of Falconet's style.

Included within this grouping is a large marble allegorical figure of *Winter* today in the State Hermitage Museum,[8] and dated to the years 1763 to 1771 on the basis

[2] Jean Pierre Antoine Tassaert, [Antwerp 1727-1788 Berlin]. Refer to HAWLEY, 1994, pp. 100-106 for informative material on the exact role of Tassaert as imitator and accomplished sculptor.

[3] Refer to *Falconet à Sèvres*, cat. 11 (p.45) for an illustrated example of one of many small-scale bathing statuettes produced as a response to Falconet's *Nymph* exhibited in the Salon 1757. This illustrated example, attributed to either one of the Broche brothers, shows a seated bathing women, much like that of the present *Seated Bather*, arguing for our model as an influence on that of such follows in the genre.

[4] Gabriel-Christophe Allegrain [Paris 1710-1795] Refer to fig. 3, *Bathing Venus*, commissioned for the gardens of Madame Du Barry at Louveciennes, and now in the Louvre, Paris [inv. MR 1747] Illustrates an obvious response to Falconet's *Nymph descending into the bath*, and proves even such close imitations were in market demand.

[5] LEVITINE, 1972, chapter IV.

[6] HILDEBRANDT, E., *E.-M. Falconet, 1716-1791*, Strassburg, 1908.

[7] Victoria and Albert Museum, London, marble, ca. 1757, about 80 cms.

[8] Falconet, *Winter*, marble, 135 cm height, ca. 1763-1771, Hermitage, Leningrad.

RELATED LITERATURE:

Falconet à Sèvres, 1757-1766; ou l'art de plaire, Musée national de Céramique, Sèvres, Réunion des Musées Nationaux, exh. cat., 6 November 2001-4 February 2002, Paris, 2001.
HAWLEY, H., 'Tassaert's "Venus", not Falconet's "Flora"', *Antologia di Belle Arti, La Scultura; Studi in onore di Andrew S. Ciechanowiecki*, 1994.
HILDEBRANDT, E., *E.-M. Falconet, 1716-1791*, Strassburg, 1908.
LEVITINE, G., *The Sculpture of Falconet*, New York, 1972.
REAU, L., *Etienne-Maurice Falconet*, 2 vols, Paris, 1922.

of extant documentation citing its commission in 1763 to the patron Madame de Pompadour and various complications including Falconet's move to Russia, explaining the unusual time taken on its completion. (fig. 2) Intended for a botanical garden, *Winter* is shown draping her robe over an outcrop of flowers, and an overturned cup implies the outside temperature in the spilled frozen water, suggested in the same polished marble technique that is seen on the present *Seated Nymph* and that of the *Nymph descending into the bath*. Interestingly, the posture of the Hermitage figure of *Winter* recalls that of the present *Seated Nymph*; the soft curve of her back, sloping shoulders, turned head and delicate rendering of the single raised foot allowing almost no question of one's compositional influence over the other. As the Hermitage *Winter* is definitively accepted as a work produced by Falconet, it would not be unlikely to propose the present composition as one originating just prior, or at the same time of Madame du Pompadour's commission, and completed preceding Falconet's call to Russia in 1766.

Fig. 2: Etienne-Maurice Falconet, *Winter*, Hermitage, St Petersburg/Bridgeman Art Library.

23 THE FOUR ELEMENTS PAYING TRIBUTE TO FRIENDSHIP

LOUIS-SIMON BOIZOT
[Paris, 1743-1809]

Circa 1783
Marble relief
45 x 60 cms
(17¾ x 23½")

Exhibited:
Salon, Paris,
1783, no. 252

Friendship stands on a column inscribed τῆ φιλια (Friendship) within a niche of drapery suspended from a tree. A wreath of myrtle, symbolising the ever-green of true friendship, crowns her head, and one arm wraps around the broken trunk of an elm tree entwined in a grape vine heavy with fruit, indicating the persistence of companionship even in times of distress. Cybele, a crowned personification of Earth, is shown in flowing drapery between two lions from her chariot, and together they bow to Friendship. Nereid emerges from the bulrushes offering up a conch shell spilling over with riches of the sea, while a triton blows a conch shell nearby; together they represent Water. Zephyr flies above, amidst swirls of clouds, and represents Air, as with one outstretched arm he clutches a handful of flowers and the other reaches for the spread wing of Jupiter in the shape of an eagle, one talon holding a bolt of lightening representative of Fire.

Boizot's propensity for the marble relief was notable as early as his days as a favoured pupil of Michel-Ange Slodtz [Paris, 1705-1764], when, in 1762, he was awarded the *Prix de Rome* for his marble relief *La Mort de Germanicus*.[1] The present relief, carved twenty years later, proves the continuity of Boizot's genius.

Exhibited at the Salon of 1783,[2] this important marble relief, *The Four Elements Paying Tribute to Friendship* (*Les Eléments rendant homage à l'Amitié*), is evocative of Boizot's most mature work and, set within a rectangular border and against a backdrop of swirling clouds, the graduated planes create a theatrical narrative of extraordinary refinement.

Contemporaneous publications on symbolism would have naturally provoked Boizot's comprehensive use of iconography,[3] while its cohesive composition is undoubtedly an impressive reflection of Boizot's imagination coupled with stylistic inspiration recalling works of Bernini[4] and Girardon. The juxtaposition of Friendship with allegorical representations of the Earth's elements is unusual, and may correspond to the thematic guidelines of the 1783 Salon. A terracotta, smaller (35 x 44 cm), but otherwise identical to the present marble, was sold by Christie's, London in 1989 as *The Four Elements paying tribute to Friendship*.[5]

Boizot simplifies the layers of symbolism through a pleasing composition and technique of carving where certain subjects, as that of Friendship, Cybele and Nereid, are treated nearly in the round, their smooth skin and well thought out anatomy and gestures, contrasting against the fine *schiacciato* details of Jupiter's

[1] LAMI, 1910, p.89.
[2] Catalogued as item number 252 in the *Livret du Salon*, Paris 1783. Boizot regularly submitted sculpture to the Salon from 1773 until three years before his death in 1806.
[3] The universality of symbols was of paramount importance in establishing an easily recognised iconographical language amongst writers, painters and sculptors, and various authoritative publications throughout Europe in the 18th century helped to solidify this means of communication. The works of Cesare Ripa were exceptional in this institution, and certain works re-published contemporaneously to Boizot's career, may have served as a useful reference for the present composition comprised almost entirely of recognisable signs and symbols. See the recently translated and illustrated edition of Ripa's 1593 edition of *Iconologia*, published in New York in 1971.
[4] For example the Nereid emerging from the water holding up a conch filled with pearls and precious smaller shells.
[5] There is record of a further terracotta relief sold at auction in Paris in 1794, possibly the same one that came up at

Christie's, London, but as it was catalogued as; *Un bas-relief en terre cuite, les Elémens qui viennent rendre homage à la Beauté et à l'Amour auxquels ils sont tous soumis* (A terracotta bas-relief, the Elements paying homage to Beauty and Love to whom they are all subject), it may not refer exactly to the subject of the present marble relief. Nonetheless, it remains possible that this terracotta sold in Paris is the same as that sold later in London, the difference resting solely on catalogue entry misinterpretation.

PUBLISHED:

Livret du Salon, Paris, 1783, no. 252.
Louis-Simon Boizot (1743-1809), Sculpteur du roi et directeur de l'atelier de sculpture á la Manufacture de Sèvres, exhib. cat., Musée Lambinet, Versailles, 23 October 2001- 24 February 2002, p. 123, no. 27, illus.

RELATED LITERATURE:

LAMI, S., *Dictionnaire des sculpteurs de l'école français au dix-huitiéme siècle*, Paris 1910.
RIPA, C., *Iconologia*, facsimile of 1758 edition by E. Maser, New York, 1971.
Louis-Simon Boizot (1743-1809), Sculpteur du roi et directeur de l'atelier de sculpture á la Manufacture de Sèvres, exhib. cat., Musée Lambinet, Versailles, Paris 2001.

feathered wings and Zephyr's muscled, outstretched body in the distance. As a tour de force this relief, *The Four Elements Paying Tribute to Friendship*, stands apart from Boizot's more characteristic academic style favoured by the court, and remains as an exceptional and vigorous testament to the sculptor's breadth of skill and aptitude for three-dimensional carving.

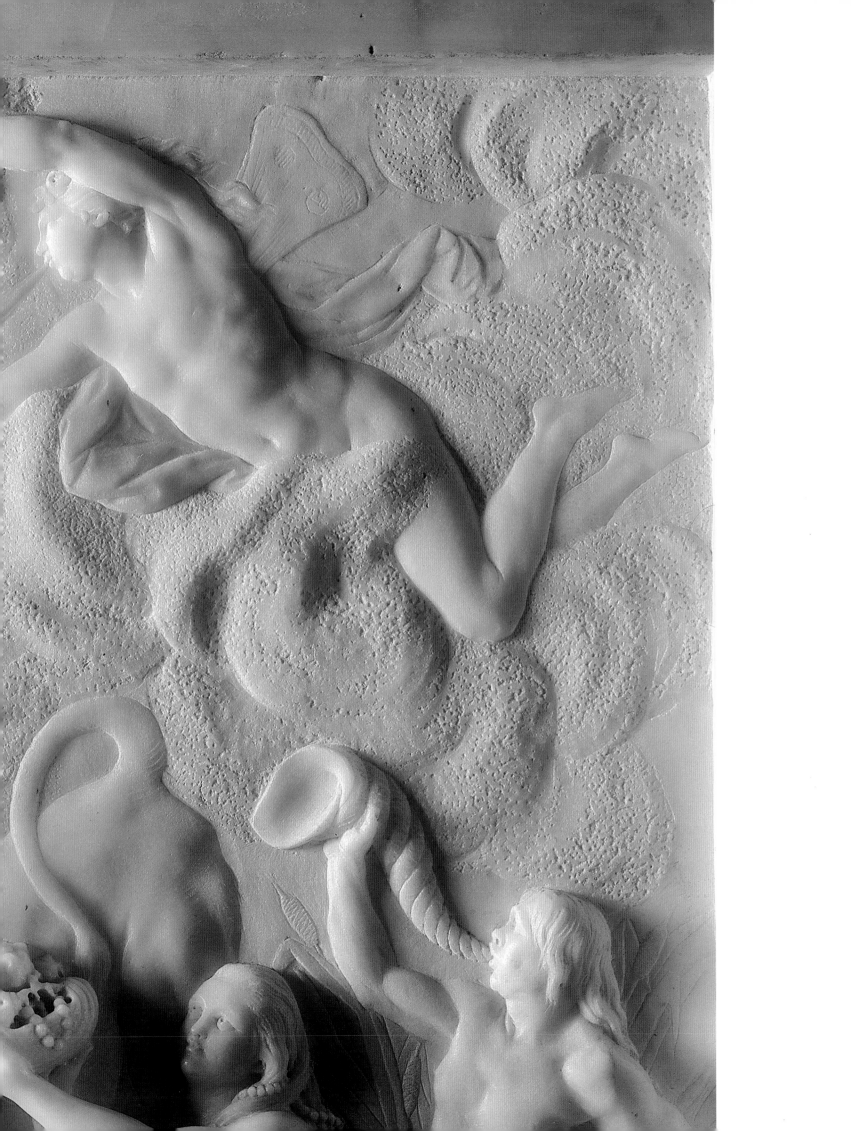

24 HEAD OF MEDUSA

ANTONIO CANOVA
[Passagno, 1757-1822]

Plaster
32.5 cm (9 $\frac{1}{5}$")
Circa 1804

[1] Many variations on the Medusa myth exist, but Ovid's account of the present iconography of the severed head of Medusa is typically the most familiar. As evidenced by various attributes on the completed group in marble, Canova extracted bits of the mythology from various sources, joining them together in what was a purely original composition of the *Triumphant Perseus*.

[2] Refer to Hugh Honour's articles on the methods of production used in Canova's workshop. HONOUR, *Burlington Magazine*, cxiv, 1972, pp. 146-59, 214-29.

[3] PAVANELLO, G., 1976, p. 104, no. 121.

The myths surrounding Medusa are many and complicated. Originating in Libya, where the Amazons worshipped her as the Serpent-Goddess, the cult of Medusa, meaning 'sovereign female wisdom', was imported to Greece where her subsequent modifications are more recognisable to us today. It is Medusa, one of the exquisite Gorgon sisters and the only mortal, that is referred to here by the severed head, specifically recalling her eventual demise by the hand of Perseus, as ordered by Athena, and recorded in Ovid's Metamorphoses. *According to Ovid, Athena was intensely jealous of Medusa's power imbued beauty, a beauty that transfixed all male eyes and turned them into stone. It is said that Perseus admired Medusa's beauty even after he held her severed head, explaining why he carried it with him in a pouch to show the Greeks. Athena frustrated over the persistence of Medusa's beauty, when even after she turned Medusa's lovely hair into a nest of seething snakes as punishment for a sacrilegious act with Poseidon, her allure was not diminished but intensified. Perseus triumphs over the sleeping Medusa, and returns to Athena on the back of a winged horse, Pegasus, that was born from the blood of Medusa's severed head and to which the wings on this plaster cast refer, and eventually presents the prized head to Athena. The severed head still possessing its powers was then wrought onto the centre of Athena's aegis and Zeus's shield as a weapon and the final symbol of Athena's victory and imprisonment of Medusa's unrivalled powers.*[1]

The present plaster cast of the severed head of *Medusa* is at once a fascinating model from Canova's studio, and an intriguing testament to the ultimate production of Canova's highly regarded *Triumphant Perseus* group. Evidenced through the dedicated study by Hugh Honour, the leading authority on Antonio Canova and his studio practice,[2] the present plaster exists as a direct cast from the now destroyed clay model of *Medusa*'s head, intended as a more permanent studio cast, and utilised in the eventual carving of the marble. There is no doubt of the importance of such casts in both the production and as a method of archiving specific compositions; a practice to which the important collection of plaster casts in the Gipsoteca at Possagno bear witness.

Canova made two marble statues of the *Triumphant Perseus*, standing with the severed head of *Medusa* in his outstretched hand. The first, completed in 1801, was acquired by Pope Pius VII for the Vatican where it has remained in the Belvedere,[3] occupying the pedestal made for the antique *Apollo Belvedere* (which Napoleon had taken to Paris). The second was contracted from Canova by the Polish Countess Tarnowska in April 1804: carved between 1806 and 1808, it is recorded by Canova himself in the 1816 list of his works.[4] Lost for years, this second statue surfaced in 1966 and was subsequently purchased by the Metropolitan Museum, New York.

As an original terracotta model of the severed head of *Medusa*, nearly identical to the present example, remains in Possagno,[5] and is believed to be that used in relation to the *Triumphant Perseus* in the Vatican, one may assume that the present plaster cast was taken from the terracotta model produced slightly later for the Tarnowska commission. It is known that terracotta models are destroyed in the process of taking piece-mould plaster casts, suggesting that Canova's terracotta *Medusa* head was not subsequently utilised in the later Tarnowska version, but instead a new working model was made, from which the present plaster cast was taken. It is important to note here that the Vatican *Perseus* was not a commission,[6] but rather the result of a long, meditated effort on the *Apollo Belvedere*, the first antique in which Canova had taken a passionate interest during a visit to Rome in 1779, and with this in mind it would not have been inconsistent that Canova did not make plaster casts beyond his original terracotta working models, as he did not, at that stage, regard the *Perseus* group as a commercial work. It was not until 1803-4 and the visit of Jan Felix Tarnowska to Rome, that, through the charms and connections of his wife Valeria, Canova promised a replica of the *Triumphant Perseus* in the Vatican.[7] It was the only further commission he accepted for this statue.

Although no ancient statue of the *Triumphant Perseus* has survived from antiquity, ultimately reflecting Canova's mythological based creativity, the severed Medusa head that Perseus holds is distinctly derived from the most admired Greek representation of the Serpent Goddess; the famous relief of the *Medusa Rondanini*, which was still in Rome at the beginning of the 19th century.[8]

[4] *Catalogo cronologico delle sculture di Antonio Canova*, Rome 1817, p.10.
[5] Gipsoteca, Possagno. Illustrated as plate 13, RAGGIO, *Connoisseur*, p 211, 1970. [31 x 36 x 30 cm]
[6] A personal impetus as documented by Canova in his *I quaderni di Viaggio* (1779-80), and later edited by BASSI, E., Venice, 1959, pp.38 and 42.
[7] The actual signed contract between Canova and Tarnowska exists in the Metropolitan, New York (inv 67.169), and explains the agreement of one replica of the Vatican *Perseus*, and subsequent payment arrangements.
[8] Marble, 1st century A.D. Munich, Glyptothek.

RELATED LITERATURE:

BASSI, E., ED., *I Quaderni di Viaggio*, Venice 1959.
HONOUR, H., 'Canova's Studio Practice', *Burlington Magazine*, cxiv, 1972.
PAVANELLO, G., *L'Opera Completa del Canova*, Milan 1976, p. 105, no. 124
PAVANELLO AND ROMANELLI ED., *Antonio Canova*, exh. cat., London, RA and V&A, 1972.
Catalogo cronologico delle sculture di Antonio Canova, Rome 1817.

25 BOULONNAISE ALLAITANT SON ENFANT (A WOMAN OF BOULOGNE SUCKLING HER CHILD)

AIMÉ- JULES DALOU
[French, 1838-1902]

Plaster
Circa 1877
65 cm (25½")

PROVENANCE:
Auguste Becker, Paris

EXHIBITED:
Galerie Delestre, *Dalou inédit*,
Paris 1978, exhib. cat., no 6.

This tender plaster group reflects a period in Dalou's career that effectively established his reputation as one of the elite 19th century sculptors, alongside Antonio Canova, Francois Rude, Auguste Rodin and Jean-Baptiste Carpeaux.[1] In the wake of Dalou's political exile to London,[2] the artist's presence in England became synonymous with a series of genre subjects, of which the present group was one, and through which Dalou expressed both an intimately human discourse and a reprise from his political affectations. The English public warmly received Dalou, and his works elicited enthusiastic praise and eager buyers at the annual Royal Academy Exhibition, at which the artist submitted a life-size terracotta of the present group in 1877.[3]

The present group of *A Mother Feeding Her Child* comes at the end of a series of Boulogne peasant girls executed during Dalou's English sojourn. Utilising the deep folds of a voluminous cloak, Dalou successfully draws the viewer into a moment of intimacy between mother and baby, where the mother, unaware of what goes on around her, simultaneously shields her newborn from the cold air and encourages it to feed from her breast. Beyond the terracotta model of this subject exhibited in 1877, a further plaster cast of similar large-scale dimensions remains in the Musée du Petit-Palais, Paris.[4]

The provenance of the present plaster to Auguste Becker furthers its importance as a working studio model, as Becker, being a favoured pupil of Dalou and close personal friend, is documented to have been given various maquettes and sketches following the sculptor's death. Close examination to the plaster's surface reveals further proof of its origin, as a pattern of tiny pencil crosses from a pointing machine, as well as various abrasions suggesting marks left by a clamp, identify the present plaster as one salvaged from Dalou's working studio, and may indicate its specific use as a model from which a marble was produced. An exhibition of these works in progress – models and drawings on paper – was compiled by the gallery owner and sculpture expert, François Delestre in Paris in 1978, in which this group *Mother Feeding Her Child* was an integral part, the overall effect of which heightened the awareness of Dalou's technique and offered a comprehensive account of the breadth of his material.[5]

The present unabashed glimpse into the natural, yet private relationship between mother and child characterised a pivotal phase in Dalou's career, and collectively served a consummate statement on the humanity of mankind, in a time when such compassion was well received. The first of Dalou's Boulonnaise series was a life-size terracotta *Paysanne français allaitant son enfant*, exhibited at

[1] Dalou's innate talent was discovered early by Carpeaux, and it was through Carpeaux's persistent encouragement that Dalou's parents allowed the young artist to enter the *Petite Ecole*. Dalou remained grateful to Carpeaux throughout his entire career, and regarded him as his true mentor.

[2] Dalou was a staunch republican, and his political sympathies were decidedly left-wing. When the Commune was established in the spring of 1871 after the French surrendered to the Prussians, Dalou became a founding member of the Fédération des Artistes. Eventually, after the fall of the Commune, he was forced into exile and departed for London by the middle of the year 1871 until the amnesty of 1879.

[3] Royal Academy 1877, no 1465.

[4] Musée du Petit-Palais, Paris, inv. no. PP 299.

[5] Refer Galerie Delestre, *Dalou inédit*, cat. no 6.

[6] Royal Academy Exhibition in 1873, no. 1540. / V&A Museum (inv nos. A.27-1912 and A.8-1993).
[7] Refer Galerie Delestre, *Dalou inédit*, cat. no 4; *Portrait of Madame Dalou*.

RELATED LITERATURE:

CAILLAUX, H., *Dalou, l'homme, l'oeuvre*, Paris 1935.
FUSCO AND JANSON, *The Romantics to Rodin*, exh. cat., Los Angeles County Museum, 1980, pp 185-199.
HUNISAK, J.M., *The Sculptor Jules Dalou*, New York and London 1977.

the Royal Academy in 1873, from which two variations stemmed, both of which are today in the Victoria and Albert Museum, London.[6] At the same time, Dalou completed a work of gritty sincerity, *Le Jour des Rameaux*, a standing peasant girl holding harvest sprigs.

The stark genre flavour of this group, *Mother Feeding Her Child*, contrasts with his parallel series of maternal subjects executed earlier, inspired by his wife and their daughter Georgette,[7] emphasising a more elegant, bourgeois nature, while retaining Dalou's propensity toward the natural maternal bond.

ABBATE, F., *La Scultura Napoletana del Cinquecento*, Rome, 1992.

AVERY, C. AND RADCLIFFE, A, ED., *Giambologna 1529-1608, Sculptor to the Medici*, exh.cat, The Arts Council of Great Britain, 1978.

AVERY, C. & LAING, A., *Fingerprints of the Artists, European Terra-Cotta Sculpture from the Arthur M. Sackler Collections,* Washington DC 1981.

AVERY, C., 'Hendrick de Keyser as a sculptor of small bronzes', reprinted in *Studies in European Sculpture*, AVERY, ed., London 1981, p. 175.

AVERY, C., *Giambologna, the Complete Sculpture*, London 1987.

AVERY, C., *Francavilla*, in J. Turner (ed.), The Dictionary of Art, London 1996.

AVERY, C., *David Le Marchand (1674-726), An Ingenious Man for Carving in Ivory*, London 1996.

AVERY C., *Museo Civico Amedeo Lia, Sculture: Bronzetti, Placchette, Medaglie.* La Spezia, 1998.

AVERY, C., 'David Le Marchand, Precursor of eighteenth-century English portrait sculpture', *The British Art Journal*, vol. 1, No.1, 1999, p.27-34.

BARNET, P., ED., *Images in Ivory; precious objects of the Gothic Age,* exh. cat., The Detroit Institute of Arts (9 March- May 11) and Walters Art Gallery (22 June-August 31), 1997.

BASSI, E., ed., *I Quaderni di Viaggio*, Venice 1959.

BEAULIEU, M., 'Description raisonnée des sculptures du Musee du Louvre', vol. II, *La Renaissance Française*, Paris, 1978, pp.152-60.

BENEZIT, E., *Dictionnaire des Peintres Sculpteurs et Graveurs*, Paris, 1999.

BENTLEY, J.H., *Politics and Culture in Renaissance Naples* , Princeton, NJ, 1987.

BISSELL, G., *Pierre Le Gros, 1666-1719,* Reading, England, 1997.

BODE, W., *The Art Collection of Mr. Alfred Beit at his residence 26 Park Lane, London,* Berlin, 1904.

BODE, W., *The Italian Bronze Statuettes of the Renaissance*, ed. and rev. by J. Draper, New York, 1980.

BORSOOK, E., *The Companion Guide to Florence*, London 1979.

BOUCHER, B., *The Sculpture of Jacopo Sansovino*, 2 vols., London 1991.

BOUCHER, B., ED., *Earth and Fire: Italian Terracotta Sculpture from Donatello to Canova,* exhibition catalogue, Yale University Press, 2001. Houston Museum of Fine Arts, 18 November 2001 –3 February 2002. Victoria and Albert Museum, London, 14 March 2002 – 7 July 2002.

BRIERE, AND LAMY, 'L'Inventaire de Barthélemy Prieur, sculpteur du roi', *Bull. Soc. Hist. Protestantisme Fr.*, xcvi-xcvii, 1949-1950, pp. 41-68.

BRYANT, J., *London's Country House Collections*, English Heritage, 1993.

BRUZELIUS AND MEREDITH, *The Brummer Collection of Medieval Art,* Duke University Press, 1991.

BURLAMACCHI, L., *Luca Della Robbia*, London, 1900.

Burlington Fine Arts Club, *Catalogue of an Exhibition of Carvings in Ivory*, London 1923.

BURNS, R. C., *Camillo Mariani: Catalyst of the Sculpture of the Roman Baroque*, Ph. D. dissertation, John Hopkins University, Baltimore 1979 (reproduced by UMI Dissertation Services, Ann Arbor, Michigan).

Cabinet de L'Art de Schulpture par le fameux sculptureur Francis van Bossuit execute en yvoire ou ébauché en terre, gravées d'aprés les dessins de Barent Graat par Mathys Pool, Amsterdam, 1727.

CAILLAUX, H., *Dalou, l'homme, l'oeuvre*, Paris 1935.

CAMBIAGI, G., *Descrizione dell'Imperiale Giardino di Boboli*, Florence 1757.

CAMINS, L., *Renaissance & Baroque Bronzes from the Abbot Guggenheim Collection*, exhibition catalogue, M.H. de Young Memorial Musem, 1988.

CARRINGTON, J.E., "A New Look at Desiderio da Firenze and the Paduan Voting Urn", *Bollettino del Museo Civico di Padova*, 73, 1984, p.109.

CASINI, C., in CIARDI, CASINI AND TOMASI, *Scultura a Pisa tra Quattro e Seicento*, Pisa, 1987.

CELIO, G., *Memorie delli nomi dell'artifici delle pitture che sono in alcune chiese, facciate e palazzi di Roma*, Naples 1638 (facsimile ed. by E. ZOCCA, Milan, 1967).

CHIPPS-SMITH, J., *German Sculpture of the Later Renaissance c. 1520-1580,* Princeton, N.J., 1994.

CRUTTWELL, M., *Luca and Andrea della Robbia and their successors*, London/New York, 1902.

DESJARDINS, A., *La vie et l'oeuvre de Jean Boulogne, d'après les manuscrits inédits recueillis par Foucques de Vagnonville,* Paris, 1883.

DEVIGNE, M., 'François Bossuit and Ignaz Elfhafen', *Burlington Magazine*, xlvii, 1925, pp. 40-46.

DHANENS, E., *Jean Boulogne*, Brussels 1956.

ENGASS, R., *Early eighteenth-century sculpture in Rome, an illustrated catalogue raisonné*, 2 vols., University Park and London, 1976, pp. 124-131.

ENGELEN, K., ed., *The Antwerp Altarpiece*, exhibition catalogue National Gallery Victoria, Antwerp, 1983.

Falconet à Sèvres, 1757-1766; ou l'art de plaire, Musée national de Céramique, Sèvres, Réunion des Musées Nationaux, exh. cat., 6 November 2001- 4 February 2002, Paris, 2001.

FORSYTH, W., "Medieval Statues of the Virgin in Lorraine related in type to the Saint-Dié Virgin", *Metropolitan Museum Studies*, 5, 1936, pp. 235-258.

FORSYTH, W., "The Virgin and Child in French Fourteenth Century Sculpture", *Art Bulletin*, 39, 1957, pp. 171-82.

FUSCO AND JANSON, *The Romantics to Rodin*, exh. cat., Los Angeles County Museum, 1980, pp 185-199.

FRANCQUEVILLE, R., *Pierre de Francqueville, Sculpteur des Médicis et du roi Henri IV*, Paris 1968.

GABORIT-CHOPIN, D, *Ivoires du Moyen Age*, Paris 1978.

GASPAROTTO, D., *Magnificenza alla corte dei Medici. Arte a Firenze alla fine del Cinquecento*, Palazzo Pitti, Florence, 1998.

GENTILINI, G., *I Della Robbia. La scultura invetriata nel Rinascimento*, Florence- n.d., 1992.

GENTILINI, G., ed., *I Della Robbia e l'arte nuova della scultura invetriata*, exhibition catalogue, Fiesole, 1998.

GURRIERI, F., AND CHATFIELD, J., *Boboli Gardens*, Florence 1972.

HASKELL AND PENNY, *Taste and the Antique*, London, 1981.

HAWLEY, H., 'Tassaert's "Venus", not Falconet's "Flora"', *Antologia di Belle Arti, La Scultura; Studi in onore di Andrew S. Ciechanowiecki*, 1994.

HILDEBRANDT, E., *E.-M. Falconet*, 1716-1791, Strassburg, 1908.

HONOUR, H., 'Canova's Studio Practice', *Burlington Magazine*, cxiv, 1972.

HUNISAK, J.M., *The Sculptor Jules Dalou*, New York and London 1977.

JACOBS, L., *Early Netherlandish Carved Altarpieces, 1380-1550*, Cambridge University Press, 1998.

KEEBLE, K., *European Bronzes in the Royal Ontario Museum*, Toronto, 1982.

KELLER-DORAIN, G., *Antoine Coysevox: Catalogue raisonne de son oeuvre*, 2 vols, Paris, 1920.

KOECHLIN, R., *Les Ivories Gothiques Français*, Paris, 1925.

KUHN, C.L., *German and Netherlandish Sculpture 1200-1800*, Harvard University Press, 1965.

LAMI, S., *Dictionnaire des sculpteurs de l'école français au dix-huitiéme siècle*, Paris 1910.

L'Art au tems des rois maudits Philippe le Bel et ses fils, 1285-1328, Galeries nationals du Grand Palais, Paris, 1998.

LEEUWENBERG AND HALSEMA-KUBES: *Beeldhouwwerk in het Rijksmuseum: Catalogus* [Sculpture in the Rijksmuseum: a catalogue], The Hague and Amsterdam, 1973.

LEVITINE, G., *The Sculpture of Falconet*, New York, 1972.

Louis-Simon Boizot (1743-1809), Sculpteur du roi et directeur de l'atelier de sculpture á la Manufacture de Sèvres, exhib. cat., Musée Lambinet, Versailles, Paris 2001.

LUCHS, A., *Tullio Lombardo and ideal portrait sculpture in Renaissance Venice, 1490-1530*, Cambridge, 1995.

MARTIN, I., ED., *Renaissance and Later Sculpture from the Thyssen-Bornemisza Collection*, London 1992.

MARQUAND, A., *Luca della Robbia*, Princeton 1914 and New York, 1972.

PAVANELLO AND ROMANELLI ED., *Antonio Canova*, exh. cat., London, RA and V&A, 1972.

PAVANELLO, G., *L'Opera Completa del Canova*, Milan 1976.

PHILIPPOVICH, E., *Elfenbein*, Munich, 1982.

PHILIPPOVICH, VON, ELFENBEIN: *Ein Handbuch fur Sammler und Liebhaber*, Munich, 1982.

PINCAS, S, *Versailles, The History of the Gardens and their Sculpture*, London, 1996.

PLANISCIG, L, *Venezianische Bildhauer der Renaissance*, Vienna 1921.

PLANISCIG, L., *Andrea Riccio*, Vienna, 1927.

POLLAK, *Raccolta Alfredo Barsanti*, Florence, 1924.

POPE-HENNESSY, J., *Italian High Renaissance and Baroque Sculpture*, London, second edition 1970.

RADCLIFFE, A., "Ricciana", *Burlington Magazine*, 124, July 1982, 412-424.

RADCLIFFE, A., "The Debasement of Images: The Sculptor Andrea Riccio and the Applied Arts in Padua in the Sixteenth Century", in *The Sculpted Object 1400-1700*, EDS. CURRIE, S. AND MOTTURE, P., Aldershot, Hants, England, 1997.

RANDALL, R., *The Golden Age of Ivory; Gothic carvings in North American collections*, New York, 1993.

REAU, L., *Etienne-Maurice Falconet*, 2 vols, Paris, 1922.

REYMOND, M., *Les Della Robbia*, Florence, 1897.

RIGONI, E., 'Giovanni Minello e la cappella dell'Arca di S Antonio', *Atti & Mem. Accad. Patavina Sci., Lett. & A.*, xlv (1953-4), pp. 90-96; also in *L'arte rinascimentale in Padova: Studi e documenti, med. & uman.*, ix (Padua, 1970), pp. 259-64

RIPA, C., *Iconologia*, facsimile of 1758 edition by E. MASER, New York, 1971.

RYDER, A., *Alfonso the Magnanimous, King of Aragon, Naples and Sicily, 1396-1458*, Oxford and New York, 1990.

SANTANGELO, *Museo di Palazzo Venezia, Catalogo delle sculture*, Rome 1954.

SCHULZ, A, 'Four New Works by Antonio Minello', *Mitteilungen des Kunsthistorischen Institutes in Florenz*, xxxi , 1987, pp. 291-326.

SCHULZ, A, 'Two New Works by Antonio Minello', *Burlington Magazine*, cxxxvii, December 1995, pp. 799-808.

SCOTT-ELLIOT, A. H., 'The Statues by Francavilla in the Royal Collection', *The Burlington Magazine*, March 1956.

SOUCHAL, F. ET AL, *French sculptors of the 17th and 18th centuries. The reign of Louis XIV. G-L*, Oxford 1981, p. 273; ibid., *Supplementary volume, A-Z*, London 1993, p. 145.

STITES, R.S., 'Leonardo da Vinci Sculptor', *Art Studies*, IV, 1926 and VIII, 1931.

THIEME BECKER - K. G. SAUR (PUBL.), *Allgemeines Künstlerlexikon...*, Leipzig & Munich, 1992-2002, 31 vols., A-Ebers

THEUERKAUFF, VON, C., *Zu Francis von Bossuit (1635-1692); Beeldsnyder in Yvoor*, Köln, 1975.

THEUERKAUFF, VON, C., *Die Bildwerke in Elfenbein des 16.-19. Jahrhunderts. Die Bildwerke der Skulpturengalerie Berlin*, Berlin 1986.

THIEME-BECKER, *Künstler-Lexikon*, vol. XXII, Germany.

THIEME, U. AND F. BECKER, EDS, *Allgemeines Lexikon der bildenden Künstler von der Antike bis zur Gegenwart*, Leipzig, vol. 33, p. 420.

THORNTON, D., *The Scholar in his Study; ownership and experience in Renaissance Italy*, New Haven, 1998.

TURNER, J. (ED.), *The Dictionary of Art*, London and New York, 1996, vol. 19, pp. 88-89, entry by F. DE LA MOUREYRE.

VASARI, G., *Le Vite de' piú eccellenti pittori scultori ed architettori*, ED. MILANESI, G., IV, Florence, 1881, pp. 305 311.

VORAGINE, J. *The Golden Legend*, vol.1, Princeton, 1993.

WARREN, J., "The Faun Who Plays on the Pipes": A New Attribution to Desiderio da Firenze, in *Small Bronzes in the Renaissance*, ed. PINCUS, D., Trustees of the National Gallery of Art, Washington, 2001.

WEIHRAUCH, H.R., *Europäische Bronzestatuetten 15.-18. Jahrhundert*, Brunswick, 1967.

WILLIAMSON, P., *The Thyssen-Bornemisza Collection; Medieval Sculpture and Works of Art*, London, 1987.

WILLIAMSON, P., *Northern Gothic Sculpture, 1200-1450*, London, 1988.

WILES, B. H., *The fountains of Florentine sculptors and their followers from Donatello to Bernini*, Cambridge, Mass., 1933.

ZURAW, S., ED., *Masterpieces of Renaissance and Baroque Sculpture from the Palazzo Venezia, Rome*, Georgia Museum of Art, October 5-November 24, Georgia, 1996.

DANIEL KATZ LIMITED

EUROPEAN SCULPTURE

New York
May 6th to May 18th 2002
19 East 66th Street
New York, NY 10021

T 212 772 8083
F 212 772 8186
E info@katz.co.uk
www.katz.co.uk

ISBN 88-7336-016-5
©, Copyright 2002/ Daniel Katz Ltd and Gli Ori, Italy

Organisation of the exhibition:	STUART LOCHHEAD
Photography:	GERRY CLIST, STAN EOST
Realised by:	Gli Ori london
Catalogue design:	PICCIA G. NERI
Scanning and repro:	SCREENSERVICE, Comeana, Italy
Printed by:	CONTI TIPOCOLOR, Calenzano, Italy

With special thanks for inspiration and advice
Mrs Barbara Latta Midulla, Charles Avery, Peta Motture, Robert Wenley, Jeremy Warren, Peter Barnet, Tamzin Phoenix- Bridgeman Library, Royal Botanical Gardens of Kew, Anthony Radcliffe, Hugh Honour, Bruce Boucher, Johannes Auersperg, Eike Schmidt, Claudio Pizzorusso, Frits Scholten, Guilhem Scherf, Alex Kader, Giancarlo Gentilini

The attributions and classifications printed in this catalogue are suggestions which, to the best of our knowledge and belief, are based on the latest art historical research, publications and consensus of opinions; the captions referring to each sculpture should help to elucidate these suggestions.